The Door in the Wall

A PLAY IN FOUR ACTS

Performance time 2 hours

ADAPTED FROM THE NOVEL,
THE DOOR IN THE WALL BY MARGUERITE DE ANGELI,
RECIPIENT OF THE JOHN NEWBERY MEDAL FOR 1950
FOR THE MOST DISTINGUISHED CONTRIBUTION
TO AMERICAN LITERATURE FOR CHILDREN

The Door in the Wall
A PLAY

By *ARTHUR CRAIG De ANGELI*
With drawings by Marguerite de Angeli

DOUBLEDAY & COMPANY, INC.
GARDEN CITY, NEW YORK

Library of Congress Catalog Card Number 68–14179
Copyright © 1968 by Doubleday & Company, Inc.
Illustration copyright 1949 by Marguerite de Angeli
All Rights Reserved
Printed in the United States of America
First Edition

AUTHOR'S NOTE

My earliest experience in the theater occurred when I was five or six years old and we were visiting our paternal grandparents in Atlantic City, New Jersey, for the summer. Our grandfather was a minstrel and had the show on the Steel Pier. My brother and I would go back stage and watch the actors make up. I can still smell the grease paint. Of course in those days, just after the first world war, the emphasis was on low comedy and song and dance. So the impressions left on our young minds were pleasant and most enjoyable. To be an actor was to desire to amuse and make people laugh.

Later, as we took part in shows and three act plays, we began to appreciate that the stage can be a force for education and training.

Our experiences with the Children's Theatre were very rewarding in the response which we invariably received from our young audiences, ranging in age from five to eighteen years. During the early thirties, children had no television nor even much radio and movies were not as sophisticated. Live actors on a stage are real and plays bring new experiences and dramatize historical events. This personal contact is so much more rewarding than any a television program could possibly bring to a viewer.

Through teaching and directing it has become evident that

more plays for children are needed. I hope both teachers and children will enjoy performing this play as much as I have enjoyed writing it.

Arthur Craig de Angeli

FOREWORD BY MARGUERITE DE ANGELI

This play, adapted from my book, *The Door in the Wall*, by our son, Arthur, adheres closely to the story as it was written and its format seems to me to be very helpful, especially to schools and amateur groups.

I have watched Arthur develop his ability to portray a character, to direct plays and now to write this one. His experience in dramatics began in high school where he appeared in a musical which the audience enjoyed greatly, judging by the applause. Later, with the graduating class, he took the part of Bottom in Shakespeare's *Midsummer Night's Dream* and again took honors for his performance.

While still in his teens, Arthur and his brother, Jack, appeared in a series of plays for children produced by Tinnin and Brown of Washington, D.C. Appearing before audiences from Philadelphia to New York and Boston, playing repertoire in such classics as *Tom Sawyer, Treasure Island, Penrod, The Three Musketeers* and *The Tempest*.

One of the plays was *Quality Street* which was produced in Brooklyn's Academy of Music. Our young daughter, Nina, took part in this production along with another child actor, Ezra Stone.

During the years of the depression, Arthur and Jack worked with various groups in and around Philadelphia. At that time Leighton Rollins came to Philadelphia and advertised for applicants to attend his School of the Theatre in New York City and Bar Harbor, Maine.

The boys, eager for employment, went for an audition and were accepted. They went to Bar Harbor and attended the summer session and later the winter session in New York City returning to Bar Harbor again for the second summer. They learned by practicing in classes and by performing in summer stock.

A number of famous people of the theatrical world came to lecture and sometimes to perform with the students. Dame Sybil Thorndike and Leslie Howard visited the New York Studio and Maude Adams and Josephine Hull were among the acting company in Bar Harbor.

Arthur and Jack later were in the Federal Theatre in Philadelphia and after that closed, Arthur became a teacher and director of adult education groups in and around the city. Arthur has been active in one or another non-professional theatre ever since those earlier days, acting and directing in dozens of plays, so he understands the problems that confront the amateur director and those who perform.

I believe he has handled these problems very well in this book.

SCENES

CHARACTERS IN THE PLAY

In Order of Appearance

NARRATOR, teller of tales

SIR JOHN DE BUREFORD, knight at court of King Edward III

ROBIN, Sir John's son

LADY MAUD, wife of Sir John, Mother of Robin

DAME ELLEN, old nurse to Robin

BROTHER LUKE, a friar, skilled in medicine

BROTHER MATTHEW, a brother friar serving at St. Mark's

LITTLE GIRL,
GEOFFREY ATTE-WATER, } survivors of the plague
CHILDREN,

JOHN-GO-IN-THE-WYND, minstrel and messenger

FIRST THIEF, highwayman

SECOND THIEF, highwayman

SHEPHERD, a local countryman

SIR PETER, squire of Lindsay Hall

LADY CONSTANCE, wife of Sir Peter

DENIS, page at Lindsay Castle

LIONEL, page at Lindsay Castle

FIRST LITTLE BOY—HENRY,
SECOND LITTLE BOY—RICHARD, } children of Sir Peter and
LITTLE GIRL—ALISON, } Lady Constance

ADAM, bowman in the service of Sir Peter

LADY MARGARET, hand maiden to Lady Constance

SENTRY, one of the Welsh soldiers

OLD WOMAN, mother of John-go-in-the-Wynd

KING, Edward the Third of England

QUEEN, Edward's Queen

NOTES ON PRODUCTION

The Narrator may be in costume and read from scroll or a public address system can be used if available.

If optional scenes are cut, the narration should be changed accordingly.

A list of easily assembled properties and diagrams for simple stage sets are given on pages 147–154.

Light flats are preferable, used inside of drapes. The doors and windows, where not used in action, can be hung on drapes (simple cutouts made of cardboard and painted). The doors can be archways. The lighting plot and sound effects are important to give atmosphere. However, these may also be uncomplicated.

Costumes are easy considering the latest fad in long hose and short jackets, the availability of wigs and simulated metallic cloth.

The text has been divided so that all dialogue is given on the right-hand pages. On the left-hand pages are the stage directions that go with the dialogue directly opposite.

(Optional—can be performed in front of curtain)

TIME *Morning*

PLACE *House of* SIR JOHN DE BUREFORD

SIR JOHN, LADY MAUD, ROBIN *and* DAME ELLEN *are on stage.* LADY MAUD *at* Right, ROBIN *Left of Center,* SIR JOHN *at* Left. DAME ELLEN *left of* SIR JOHN.

PROLOGUE

NARRATOR   The place is England in the middle of the fourteenth century—about 1334. We are in the house of Sir John de Bureford in London. The time is morning in the month of January.

SIR JOHN (*Man to man*) My son, the time for parting has come. Within a few days, I and my men-at-arms, must join the King to do battle with the Scots who have invaded our country to the North.

ROBIN (*Wistfully.*) Yes, my father. Would that I might go with you.

SIR JOHN   Nay, your journey is to Lindsay and Sir Peter's household where you will serve as page and learn the ways of a gentle knight. Your mother and I have arranged for John-the-Fletcher to come for you and take you to Lindsay Castle.

LADY MAUD   My son (*Crosses to him, turns him to her, takes him by chin*) you are now ten years old and no longer to be looked after by womenfolk. It is time now for you to be taught the ways of men and arms. At Lindsay Castle you will be away from danger of the plague that is spreading and I must obey the wish of the Queen to attend her as lady-in-waiting, for she is ill and in need of my care.

STAGE DIRECTION

ROBIN *reaches to her and puts his arms around her.*

SIR JOHN *crosses to* ROBIN, *pauses, puts hand on* ROBIN'S *shoulder.*

SIR JOHN *embraces* LADY MAUD *and exits up Right.*

Ad lib as they go toward exit Left. ROBIN *follows.*

Dim Out

CURTAIN

ROBIN   Yes, Mother, but I shall be so lonely.

SIR JOHN   Farewell, my son, forget not to be brave. Good-bye, dear wife (*Crosses to her on line*) God willing we shall meet again before long.

LADY MAUD   Now you are a great lad. (*Trying to be more cheerful, takes* ROBIN *by shoulders and pushes him away gently*) Dame Ellen will be here with the cook and Gregory to care for you until John-the-Fletcher arrives. He should be here in a day or two. (*Crosses Left to* ELLEN) Now Ellen, see you that the lad eats well, and keep him from the street where the plague threatens. Keep him clothed in woolen hose.

TIME   *Midday in March*

PLACE   ROBIN'S *bedroom in his father's house*

As the curtain rises, there are street sounds offstage, bells ringing, and boys and girls shouting and running through street. ROBIN *drags himself up against the headboard of bed. He struggles to edge of bed, trying to lift his legs one by one with his hands. He sighs loudly and falls back against pillow.*

There are sounds of wagons and horses in the street, etc., sounds offstage of DAME ELLEN *coming with food, and doors opening and closing.* ROBIN *settles down in bed and pulls covers over his head.* DAME ELLEN *approaches bed from upstage Right. She leans over him to see if he is asleep.* ROBIN *faces audience and pretends to be asleep. Pantomime shows* ROBIN *is spoiled by* ELLEN *as she tries to pull covers from over his head.*

ACT I

Scene I

NARRATOR While the plague rages in the city of London, England, in the year 1334, Robin, son of Sir John de Bureford, lies ill in his father's house, crippled by a strange malady which affects his back and legs. His father has gone off to the wars with King Edward III, more than a month before. His lady mother has left to be in the Queen's service, and Robin is supposed to be en route to Lindsay Castle in the North where he was to serve as a page in his first step toward knighthood. As the curtain rises, we see Robin still abed, recuperating. The time is midday on a cold March day.

ROBIN (*Disgusted*) Like dough.

DAME ELLEN (*Coaxing. Her voice is harsh and flat*) Turn over, do, there's a good lad.

STAGE DIRECTION

She comes around bed, sits by ROBIN *so as to be able to feed him. She pulls him up to a position against pillows and arranges bedclothes around him, coaxing him to eat.*

ROBIN *buries face in pillows.* ELLEN *tugs at coverlet.*

ROBIN *flings his arms sending porridge out of her hands, all over her.*

ELLEN *bursts into loud weeping and rushes from room up Right, wiping porridge off her face with apron.*

ROBIN *hurls empty bowl after* ELLEN's *exit.*

BLACKOUT
to Signify Time Lapse

DAME ELLEN (*Pleading*) Come lad, try this. . . . Wilt not have this good porridge all with honey spread?

DAME ELLEN Sweet lad (ROBIN *will not turn or answer. He elbows her away.* ELLEN *tries to coax him, offering him spoonful*) 'Twill give thee strength and mend those ailing limbs. Come, my pretty lad.

DAME ELLEN Wicked boy! (*She screams*) No more will I serve thee! Scarce able to stand have I been this day, yet have I been faithful. (*Sobs*) But I am a free woman and can go my way. Just wait and see when more victuals are brought thee! Ungrateful wretch!

ROBIN (*Shouting after* ELLEN *as she leaves*) You will come back! And you'd better bring me something I like if you want me to eat it!

TIME   *Evening of the same day*

PLACE   ROBIN'S *bedroom*

As light comes up on scene, ROBIN *is sitting up in bed with bedclothes around him trying to keep warm. There are street sounds and noises offstage and people running shouting, "Bring out your dead," etc.* ROBIN *attempts to get up in bed but falls as his legs are useless, struggles, falls back exhausted into bed, and pulls up covers around him. Everything becomes quiet for considerable pause. Finally we hear doors opening and closing and steps in the passageway offstage up Right.* ROBIN *pulls covers around him and shows fear. Finally door up Right opens very slowly and* BROTHER LUKE *enters carrying basket in upstage hand. He comes toward bed and pauses for effect.* ROBIN *is afraid to look at him not knowing what to expect.*

BROTHER LUKE *appears to be a sinister figure until he throws back his cowl. He speaks in a low, modulated voice as he approaches the bed.*

ROBIN *has drawn himself up in bed during this speech. He reacts to word "fish." Then he shows interest in the basket of food.* BROTHER LUKE *starts to take things from it. He helps* ROBIN *to sit up and makes him comfortable during speech.*

ACT I
Scene II

NARRATOR   But Dame Ellen does not come back. One hour goes by, then another, and another. As the afternoon draws into evening, it becomes colder and colder. By the changing sounds in the street, and the bells, Robin knows that time for vespers has come. He hears sounds in the passage. Perhaps it is Dame Ellen returning.

BROTHER LUKE   Good eve, my son, I am Brother Luke, a wandering friar, newly come to St. Mark's. I have brought thee food and, cause 'tis Friday, fish.

BROTHER LUKE   A poor widow, who twice a week is fed from our hospice, told me of thy need. She said that Dame Ellen, who lately served thee, has this very day been taken of the plague. . . . She it was told us that all thy servants, too, are fled, because of the plague, and some are dead of it. Dame Ellen told thee not, pitying thee. Now, be a good lad and take thy supper.

ROBIN *obediently eats as the friar feeds him.* BROTHER LUKE *talks quietly while* ROBIN *eats, taking time to tell story.*

During ROBIN's *long speech,* BROTHER LUKE *fetches water in basin and washes him and makes him comfortable, rubbing* ROBIN's *back, etc. Through this speech,* BROTHER LUKE *makes sympathetic sounds and gestures.*

BROTHER LUKE   It is well known that thy father hath of his goodness given money to St. Mark's. So, to St. Mark's I will take thee and will care for thee in mine own quarters because all other beds and places are already taken by those in the parish who have great need. Even the corridors are filled and the cloisters lined with pallets to make beds for the sick.

ROBIN (*Woefully*) But I cannot walk. See you, my two legs are as useless as if they were logs of wood. . . . (*Tearfully*) My father is with the King at the Scottish wars and with him are all his men-at-arms. . . . My lady mother has been commanded to attend upon Her Majesty the Queen. . . . It is supposed by them that I am now a page in the household of Sir Peter de Lindsay at his castle in the North. (*Tries to compose himself*) John-the-Fletcher was to have come for me in March, before the Feast of St. Gregory. Instead, a messenger came on that day to say that John-the-Fletcher had been set upon by thieves and lay wounded in the hospice at Reading. . . . (*Pause*) He came later to fetch me, but found me thus, unable to walk or ride. (*Pause*) He brought a surgeon who said I had not the plague but some other malady. The messenger told Ellen to feed me well and that he would return. He came not again nor did John-the-Fletcher.

BROTHER LUKE   Alas, because of the plague all the physicians are working night and day. Either the surgeon himself has been taken by the plague or he has been so busy caring for others he has not been able to return. As for John-the-Fletcher, he may have gone out of the city gate and not been allowed to re-enter, for they are keeping

BROTHER LUKE *opens chest for underlinen and hose, hood with long peak and warm cloak.* BROTHER LUKE *dresses* ROBIN *as he talks.*

ROBIN *wonders what* BROTHER LUKE *is trying to tell him.*

ROBIN *is not sure he understands.*

BROTHER LUKE *puts arms under* ROBIN, *hoists him on back, carrying bundle of* ROBIN's *clothes and basket in one hand and steadying* ROBIN *with the other. They exit up Right.*

CURTAIN

strangers out now. . . . (*Trying to cheer* ROBIN) Fear not for the manner of our going to St. Mark's. Tethered in the courtyard is a jennet ready saddled with blankets whereon thou'lt ride softly. Walking beside thee, I shall support thee, and so we shall go through Knightrider Street and Giltspur to Ludgate and then toward Smoothfield where stands St. Mark's. . . . (*Pause*) Dost remember the long wall that is about the garden of thy father's house?

ROBIN   Yes, of course, why?

BROTHER LUKE   Dost remember, too, the wall about the Tower or any wall? (*Pause*) Have they not all a door somewhere?

ROBIN   Yes?

BROTHER LUKE   Always remember that (*Emphatically*). Thou hast only to follow the wall far enough and there will be a door in it.

ROBIN   (*Nodding slowly*) I will remember.

BROTHER LUKE   (*Briskly*) The evening damp creeps up from the Thames and though the days are longer now, it is still early in the season. Good English wool will keep thee warm. Now for the hood.

ROBIN   (*Anxiously*) Will I come back home soon? Will a message be sent to my father? Or to my mother?

BROTHER LUKE   Be comforted, my child. As soon as the plague is somewhat quieted in London, a messenger will be sent to thy father. Meanwhile, we shall care for thee. Now, rest on me, my son.

STAGE DIRECTION

TIME *Ten weeks later*

PLACE *Garden of St. Mark's*

Two or three people are lying on mats or are propped up against wall, upstage. ROBIN *is in trundle cart (wheelbarrow) and is whittling on boat downstage Right. Carpenter's bench is at upper Left. There is sound of singing offstage—plain song.* ROBIN *sings with them.* BROTHER LUKE *enters up Right, carrying bowl of food.*

BROTHER LUKE *hands bowl to Robin as he picks up boat. Robin does not eat.*

ROBIN *has set the bowl down and reaches for the boat, anxious to continue carving.* BROTHER LUKE *holds it away from him and picks up the bowl and gently hands it back to* ROBIN *who then reluctantly starts to eat.*

ROBIN *eats as* BROTHER LUKE *speaks.*

ACT II

Scene I

NARRATOR   Brother Luke has cared for Robin as if he were a little child, bringing him food and washing him and changing his clothes. Ten weeks have passed. It is a lovely May morning in the garden of St. Mark's.

BROTHER LUKE   (*Pauses to observe, nods approvingly*) Time passes quickly when thy hands are busy. Dost like to whittle?

ROBIN   Yes, who does not? See the sailboat I am making?

BROTHER LUKE   That piece of soft pine makes easy carving. I see this is to be a sailing boat after all, and not a barge. It is somewhat awry, with the bow aslant from the stern, but it hath an air (*Turning it and examining it*) as if it had been battling a storm.

BROTHER LUKE   (*Coaxing*) Eat thy soup. It is made of good mutton in which bay and marigold have been seethed. Brother Michael grows these fragrant herbs in the garden. Bay is tasty and gives good appetite.

ROBIN   (*Grudgingly*) It does taste good.

33

ROBIN *shrugs but continues eating as* BROTHER LUKE *urges him.*

BROTHER LUKE *proceeds to show* ROBIN *how to make sails, etc.*

BROTHER LUKE   Marigold is said to be of value against poor sight and angry words. It is said 'twill draw evil humours out of the head, and the flowers make fair garlands for maidens because of their golden color.

ROBIN *(Pouting)* I care not for soppy food nor am I a maiden who wishes garlands for my hair.

BROTHER LUKE *(Cheerfully, taking things from his gown)* I have brought thee linen for sails and pieces of yarn for rigging. And here is a bit of ribbon for a pennant to fly from the masthead.

ROBIN *(Eagerly)* I should like to really carve a figure like the dwarfs and gargoyles on the roof bosses of my father's house!

BROTHER LUKE *(Starting to rub* ROBIN's *back and leg)* Patience, my son, it takes great skill to carve figures like that. *(Pauses)* Why not make a simple cross. 'Twill be fit to hang over thy cot if 'tis well made and smoothly finished.

ROBIN   Shall I make it of pine as I have the boat?

BROTHER LUKE   I have some pieces of walnut which I saved from pruning the tree that stands by the well. It is weathered, for it hath lain in the sun and rain these many months.

ROBIN   And how shall I fasten the pieces of the cross together? Shall I nail it then? Or how shall it be done?

BROTHER MATTHEW *enters, stops to look at* ROBIN, *then crosses to workbench up Left.*

Boys and girls enter down Left. GEOFFREY ATTE-WATER *is on crutches.* LITTLE GIRL *speaks, running to* BROTHER LUKE.

At left of cart, watching as BROTHER LUKE *starts to cross up turning to Right carrying* ROBIN *on his back,* GEOFFREY *reaches up to smack* ROBIN *on rear.*

BROTHER LUKE *turns back to see what has happened.*

BROTHER LUKE   When thou'rt ready for that, Brother Matthew will show thee. (*He gestures to* BROTHER MATTHEW *over Left who nods and smiles*) Thou shalt make it smooth and well proportioned, for it will be a keepsake and not a toy like the little boat. Doing things well is part of the joy in making things.

ROBIN (*Pleading*) Brother Luke, will you teach me to write? We were taught singing at the Brothers' school but I know not writing. Will you teach me then?

BROTHER LUKE   Yes, my son, truly I will when there are not so many people to care for. (*Starting to lift* ROBIN) But come now, back to thy cot. First, we shall stop to say a prayer in the chapel for thy strengthening.

LITTLE GIRL (*Coaxing*) Carry me, too, please carry me!

BROTHER LUKE (*Patting her on the head*) Later, my child, later. Come with us now to chapel.

GEOFFREY   Good eve, Brother Crookshanks, I see I have good company.

ROBIN (*Shouting angrily*) Keep your filthy hands off me, lout! Varlet! I am no more crookshanked than you!

GEOFFREY (*Jeering*) Ho! Ho! Ho! Just listen to him. (*Elaborate bow*) Your Lordship—beggin' your Lordship's pardon, Sir.

ROBIN *has climbed down from cart carefully holding onto the side, and reaches toward* GEOFFREY'S *crutch, puts it under his shoulder, and tries a step or two.* BROTHER LUKE, *noting his effort and approving, pats his shoulder.*

BROTHER LUKE *pantomimes this. All the children laugh at his antics.*

BROTHER LUKE (*Laughs at* ROBIN's *outburst*) Now, then, Robin. (*Setting* ROBIN *back on trundle cart and scolding* GEOFFREY) Fie on thee for an impertinent lad! Still, "Crookshanks" he is, truly. His legs will be as good as thine one day, and then he shall keep thee company right enough on his feet. (*Turning to* ROBIN *smiling*) The lad meant no offense when he called thee "Crookshanks," Master Robin. 'Tis but the way we all are named; for some oddity we have, or for where we live, or for what we do. This boy is called Geoffrey Atte-Water, because he lives by the River Fleet and tends to the conduit there with his father. He was so called before he limped as he does now.

ROBIN Oh, I wondered why he is not called Geoffrey Crook-shanks. Now I understand.

BROTHER LUKE Now, I was called Chaucer, because my father was a shoemaker but since I have taken a vow to be a monk and to serve our Lord wherever I am most needed, I have taken the name of Luke, the physician in the Gospel.

ROBIN (*Comprehending*) And my father is Sir John de Bureford because he came from that place. Is that the way of it?

BROTHER LUKE That is the right of it. When Geoffrey called thee "Crookshanks" he said it because thy legs are *thy* legs and bent ones. Richard Smaltrot is he with the short step, (*Pantomimes small steps*) and not Richard Crowfoot whose feet splay out like fans.

CURTAIN

BROTHER LUKE   Now we go to our prayers. (BROTHER LUKE *takes* ROBIN *on his back.* ROBIN *hands crutch back to* GEOFFREY *and as they exit across to Center and up,* ROBIN *speaks.*)

ROBIN (*Ruefully*) What have I to be thankful for? How will my father like a son who is called "Crookshanks"?

BROTHER LUKE (*Comforting him as they exit up Right*) Never mind, he'll love thee whether thou walk'st straight or not.

STAGE DIRECTION

TIME   *One month later*

PLACE   *Garden of St. Mark's*

BROTHER LUKE *enters up* Right, *carrying* ROBIN *on his back and brings him downstage* Right, *having fun with him.*

BROTHER LUKE *pretends along with him and gallops back and forth snorting and neighing.*

BROTHER MATTHEW *enters up* Right *and stops to enjoy the horseplay and then crosses to his bench.*

Carrying on the play, ROBIN *pretends to beat him on the back though* BROTHER LUKE *is standing beside him.*

ROBIN *pretends to whack off* BROTHER LUKE'S *head with an imaginary sword.*

ACT II

Scene II

NARRATOR   Another month has gone by and as the days grow warmer the plague abates. Fewer people come to St. Mark's for care and those who are well have gone to their homes. It is another lovely day in the garden at St. Mark's.

BROTHER LUKE (*Happily*) Keep thy hold strong! 'Tis good exercise for thine arms to make thee hold on! (*He bounces him up and down and* ROBIN *laughs gleefully*) And will be good exercise for me, too, carrying a great lad of ten!

ROBIN (*Laughing*) More! More! Be my horse. I am a knight and you are my horse.

BROTHER LUKE (*Sets* ROBIN *on cart, speaks breathlessly*) Whew, I cannot carry thee as easily as when I first brought thee here to St. Mark's, I vow. (*He gasps*) Thou hast gained five stone.

ROBIN   What! You varlet. . . . Old horse, we shall make hound's meat of you! Whee! Off with your head!

ROBIN *picks up pieces of wood from bottom of cart.*

BROTHER MATTHEW *crosses down to them and examines the piece of cross.*

BROTHER LUKE *crosses upstage and exits.*

BROTHER MATTHEW *pushes* ROBIN *in cart across and up Left of Center toward his bench.* ROBIN *shows great interest in things on bench.*

BROTHER LUKE (*Breathlessly*) Get to thy whittlings. A little of that horseplay quite winds me. (*Continuing as he gains breath*) But I'm glad for thy mischief, for it is a sign thou'rt well again.

ROBIN (*Happily*) See you, Brother Luke, how I am making my cross from the sticks of walnut you brought me?

BROTHER LUKE (*Examining the piece, approving, turning it over and over*) It is indeed a fine bit of work and it keeps thy hands busy.

ROBIN (*Puzzled*) But how to fasten the pieces I know not. (*Placing them together*) Could you tell me, Brother Luke?

BROTHER LUKE (*Reassuring*) Brother Matthew will show thee and will welcome thee to his workbench when thou'rt weary of sitting here. (*Raising his voice*) Wilt look after Robin, Brother Matthew?

BROTHER MATTHEW I shall. I see he is one of us in the use of his hands.

BROTHER LUKE (*To* ROBIN) I have somewhat in mind for thee.

ROBIN (*To* BROTHER MATTHEW) 'Twill be a cross when 'tis done. (*Pause*) But I know not how to fasten the pieces. Could you show me how, Brother Matthew?

BROTHER MATTHEW I will, surely. But I have better tools. Come we'll bring thee nearer where we can reach them.

BROTHER MATTHEW *smiles at* ROBIN *and turns back to his bench where he takes up a crutch that he is making for* ROBIN. *He holds it up looking at* ROBIN. *The audience sees it.* ROBIN *does not.*

Here we can have an interval of music from chapel offstage. ROBIN *lifts his head to listen and sings with them. All seems peaceful as both* ROBIN *and* BROTHER MATTHEW *are working hard.*

(Note: One piece of the cross should be sawed half through so as to break easily.)
ROBIN *is peacefully working and whistling responding to bird calls, etc. He stands up beside cart and tries a couple of steps, always holding on to the cart. Looking off to see birds,* ROBIN *decides to settle down to work again. There is a long quiet pause—then the explosion! As* ROBIN *is carving, the tool slips and ruins his work. His face is drawn into a black cloud of anger. Only his condition prevents him from stalking off out of the garden.* ROBIN *makes an attempt at jumping up but sinks back. He explodes!*

BROTHER MATTHEW (*Picking up chisel*) Here, try this. Take care it has an edge to it.

ROBIN   Oh, how fine it is and how sharp! (*Testing edge*)

BROTHER MATTHEW   Now, we shall make a half joint, so, (*He shows* ROBIN, *placing pieces together*) and fit it tightly, cutting each piece only halfway through the wood, so the crosspiece will just fit into the upright one.

ROBIN (*Impatiently*) But, how will they stay together?

BROTHER MATTHEW (*Patiently*) We shall secure it with fish glue, and the dust which comes from using the rubbing stone, to polish the wood, will fill in the least crack and make all smooth.

ROBIN (*Getting down to work*) Thank you, Brother Matthew.

ROBIN   BLAST!

STAGE DIRECTION

He throws the broken pieces across stage Left in general direction of BROTHER MATTHEW *and the chisel after them. (A property wooden chisel should be used.)* BROTHER MATTHEW *ducks elaborately.*

BROTHER MATTHEW *crosses down to* ROBIN.

ROBIN *takes step or two toward* BROTHER MATTHEW.

BROTHER MATTHEW *looks at* ROBIN *quietly as if to calm him.* ROBIN *slowly recovers himself and then, ashamed, buries his face in his arms on back of cart.*

ROBIN *looks up to see* BROTHER MATTHEW *give him a smile of encouragement and cross to bench again.* BROTHER LUKE *enters up Right, crosses down carrying scrolls, ink pot and pen to* ROBIN *and speaks, as if nothing has happened or as if he has noticed nothing.*

ROBIN *sits down snuffling and wiping his tears.*

ROBIN (*Shouting*) Treacherous misguided tool! I'll have no more of you.

BROTHER MATTHEW (*Quietly*) 'Tis not the tool that is at fault but thine own unskilled hands.

ROBIN (*Roaring*) Think you I am but a carpenter's son and apprentice!

BROTHER MATTHEW (*Quietly and deliberately*) If thou'rt to learn to use tools, patience and care are better teachers than a bad temper.

BROTHER MATTHEW (*Pats* ROBIN's *shoulder comfortingly*) Tomorrow is another day. Take thy rest for now, and thou wilt do better work next time. (*He pauses, looking up as he hears* BROTHER LUKE *coming*) Here is Brother Luke coming to care for thee!

BROTHER LUKE   Master Robin, today we open another door in the wall. We shall begin to teach thee to read and to write. We must teach thy hands to be skillful in many ways.

ROBIN *pulls himself together, trying to gain his composure.*

BROTHER LUKE *winks at* BROTHER MATTHEW *who looks up and nods.*

ROBIN *dictates as* BROTHER LUKE *writes, with* BROTHER LUKE *holding up hand once in a while to slow* ROBIN's *words.*

ROBIN (*Pleading*) Oh, do teach me to write . . . how to make the letters . . . I long to learn.

BROTHER LUKE (*Decisively*) We shall begin today. We shall divide the days into teaching the mind and teaching thy hands, then weariness shall not give thee excuse for discouragement.

ROBIN I wish to send a letter to my father. (*Wiping away the tears*)

BROTHER LUKE I have brought quill and parchment to pen a letter for thee. (BROTHER LUKE *settles down beside* ROBIN) It so happens that a hundred men-at-arms and a hundred foot soldiers have sworn to serve loyally their King and the city of London and are leaving for the Scottish border tomorrow. With them goes a minstrel well known to us, one John-go-in-the-Wynd. He will gladly carry thy letter and put it into thy father's hands.

ROBIN Say this—
Sir John de Bureford from his son Robin. Greetings. It is a fine thing that your son Robin is left to the care of strangers. Had it not been for Brother Luke, who is writing this letter, I should be dead. (ROBIN *warms to his tale of woe*) As you know, my lady mother had been commanded to attendance on the Queen and I was left to await the coming of John-the-Fletcher in the care of Dame Ellen. (*He stands shakily holding on to cart*) Just before the Feast of Matthew, the 24th of February, I woke one morning unable to rise from my bed, being very ill. (*He*

BROTHER LUKE *finishes letter and signs with flourish.*

BROTHER LUKE *starts to read as light falls, indicating passage of time.*

Dim Out as BROTHER LUKE *Reads*

CURTAIN

lets go of cart then grabs it again) So that when John-the-Fletcher came to take me to my Lord Peter de Lindsay's castle in Shropshire, I was unable to go. Wherefore he sent a physician to care for me, who came not again, (*He takes step away and quickly turns back to hold on to cart again*) but left me as before in Dame Ellen's care. The men-at-arms are with you, as well you know. The house servants, even old Gregory, have left our service for the plague had them. Ellen, too, was taken of it and I was left alone and helpless. (*Gestures to legs*) My legs were as useless as two sausages. But now I can bear my weight upon my feet, though I cannot stand alone, nor can I straighten my back. I am somewhat better and in the care of this good Brother Luke at St. Mark's. How, then, shall I do? Send me a letter, I beg you, and farewell.

BROTHER LUKE   Now, attend, I shall read this slowly, pointing out each letter and word so this may be thy first lesson.

ROBIN   Oh, you have made it look like poetry. (*Still standing,* ROBIN *looks over* BROTHER LUKE's *shoulder.*)

BROTHER LUKE (*Wryly*) Yes, but when it is read to thee, 'twill not sound like poetry, I'll vow. Thou hast not minced words in thy. letter.

TIME   *Morning at end of September*

PLACE   *Garden of St. Mark's*

BROTHER LUKE *enters from down Left, carrying* ROBIN, *who has no shirt on. Other children, carrying* ROBIN's *shirt strung up on two sticks by the shoulders, troop after them led by* GEOFFREY—*all excited—speaking at once of how well* ROBIN *has learned to swim.*

The others ad lib "He beat me," "Did you see him?" They talk to each other "He surprised us surely!" "Wasn't he good," etc.

BROTHER LUKE *stands* ROBIN *down Right of Center by cart, and starts rubbing his back and arms with shirt.*

ACT II

SCENE III

NARRATOR   Three months have elapsed and Robin has been kept busy every day with his carving and learning to read and write. Brother Luke has taught him many things— about the stars, about far countries, about the Holy Land where Crusaders fought for the tomb of our Lord, about Greece and Rome. He has told him of the Roman Legions who had come to Britain centuries before, and of Saxon and Danish kings who had in turn ruled the land. But of all the things Brother Luke taught him, and of all the happy hours Robin spent learning from him, the happiest of all was the day he learned to swim with the other children. From then on, even on cloudy or rainy days and when the weather was quite cool, Robin was taken for his daily swim.

ROBIN (*Shivering*) How cold the water! Did you see me dive? I thought I'd never come up. . . .

GEOFFREY (*Enthusiastic*) Why, Robin swims as well as any of us! He even beat us *all* to the weir and back today.

BROTHER LUKE   I see thou'rt getting stronger. It may be that the swimming and this rubbing helps thee. How, I know not, but it may stir up thy blood and make thee more comfortable.

GEOFFREY *leans on cart as he hands crutches to* ROBIN.

ROBIN *puts crutches under his arms and goes slowly but easily across stage and back. The children cheer.*

ROBIN *is triumphant, beaming.* BROTHER LUKE *steadies him.*

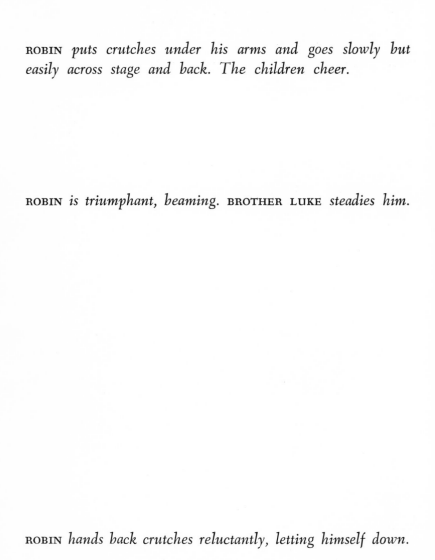

ROBIN *hands back crutches reluctantly, letting himself down.*

ROBIN (*Triumphant*) Today I feel that soon I shall walk!

GEOFFREY   Here, try my crutches again.

ROBIN   Yes, let me try.

CHILDREN   Good! Well done, Robin . . . (*etc.*)

BROTHER LUKE (*Skeptical*) Whether thou'lt walk again I know not.

ROBIN (*Shouts*) I shall! I shall! Let me go awhile by myself!

BROTHER LUKE (*Calmly*) God's good time, his sunshine and the love that is borne thee, all are healing. A bright spirit helps, too, and that thou hast.

ROBIN (*Impetuous*) I must get well before my father returns from the wars.

BROTHER LUKE (*Warning*) We must teach thy mind to go about whether thy legs will carry thee or no . . . (*Pause*) . . . (*Reminding him*) Reading is another door in the wall, dost understand, my son?

ROBIN (*Smiling and nodding*) Yes, I see now what you mean by the door in the wall.

BROTHER LUKE *takes scroll from cart, settles children around him, and opens it.*

BROTHER LUKE *examines the children to see how they are taking it.* BROTHER MATTHEW *enters from down Right.*

BROTHER MATTHEW *gestures off Right.* JOHN-GO-IN-THE-WYND, *mintral harp slung over shoulder, enters down Right.* ROBIN *greets him.* JOHN *crosses down to cart and kneels by* ROBIN.

JOHN *has taken small scroll from doublet and hands it to* ROBIN.

BROTHER LUKE   We shall read together. (*Pause*) Here is somewhat of the earth and stars that Brother Hubert has set down. How they go in their seasons so that in summer when we rise for the midnight office Orion is here. Yet in winter, at the same hour, he is over there. (*He stops to point in different directions overhead as he goes on*) Some say that the earth extends just so far, then droppeth off into a vast sea. Perhaps it is so, I know not. But if it be so, how does it happen the stars are out again in their season? Who knows? Not I. But someday we shall know all.

BROTHER MATTHEW   A messenger has come for young Robin from his father.

JOHN-GO-IN-THE-WYND   Good young master. (*He rises as he speaks*) This letter I bring from thy noble father in all haste. For long I could not find him for that the battle did go first to one place then to another. And the Scots be so fierce in fighting that often the battle went against our side.

ROBIN   And how goes it now?

JOHN   It goes well now and here is thy letter.

ROBIN (*Eagerly*) Is my father alive? Is he well and safe?

JOHN (*Reassuring*) He is well and safe.

ROBIN *takes letter, tries to read, and is helped by* BROTHER LUKE *whom he questions on larger words.*

BROTHER LUKE *takes over reading more quickly but* ROBIN *naturally wants to see too—they share the letter.*

ROBIN *shows excitement at news.*

BROTHER LUKE *looks up at* JOHN-GO-IN-THE-WYND *who nods and smiles.*

BROTHER LUKE *looks up and shakes head sadly.*

ROBIN (*Reading slowly*) Son of John de Bureford from his
father. Greetings. (ROBIN *reads laboriously as he tries to
make out some of the larger words*) It grieves me, my
son, more than I can tell you to know that you are ill . . .
I thank heaven it is not the plague you have had, for
that has slain more men than battle, besides the women
and children it has taken toll of . . . It shocked me to
learn that you had been left to the care of strangers . . .
Your mother would hardly bear it if I should tell her,
but I will not . . . She is with the Queen who is in
delicate health. I dare not say where, lest this letter fall
into unfriendly hands. . . .

She supposes that you are far away from London, in Shropshire . . . it is well. Let her continue to think so for in truth
you soon will be, God willing and your health permitting,
for I have requested the Prior to arrange your journey with
all speed . . . You will travel in care of Brother Luke and
John-go-in-the-Wynd.

BROTHER LUKE (*Pointing out words to* ROBIN *as he reads,
accenting them*) I had a message from Sir Peter . . . only
the day before your letter reached me . . . asking what
had happened to you, for John-the-Fletcher never returned
. . . Some evil befell him surely . . . for he was an
honorable servant. Sir Peter was wounded while bringing up forces to my aid . . . so sorely wounded that he has
been taken to a castle nearby where he will stay until he
is able to be taken home . . . The Scots are being slowly

Each one listening reacts to words.

This is good news.

This is better news.

BROTHER LUKE *gives rueful laugh, others join him.*

BROTHER LUKE *gives orders to other children to perform various services; to the stable for horses to be saddled, to* ROBIN'S *room to bundle up clothing, etc. One child goes up Right, one up Center and one down Left.*

BROTHER MATTHEW *exits off Left.*

pushed back and we are gaining ground . . . since receiving the added help from London and the nearby towns. The King hopes for a peace by the Sacrament of Christmas but the Scots are a stubborn race. I trust that you are improving in health, my son, and go in God's Grace. So, Farewell . . . Your Father, Sir John de Bureford, Thursday after the Feast of John the Baptist.

BROTHER LUKE (*Pause*) What think you of that, Master Robin?

ROBIN (*He reaches for letter, and shouts*) Hurrah!

BROTHER LUKE We shall leave at once. Geoffrey, go to Brother Andrew in the kitchen and ask him to prepare us some food for our journey.

BROTHER MATTHEW (*Busily*) I shall prepare a basket of fruit. 'Twill be good for noon quench when there is no ale to be had, and will mind thee to be thankful for God's gifts.

JOHN-GO-IN-THE-WYND (*Warningly*) There are over a hundred English miles to go and frost is not far off, so we must go steadily.

BROTHER LUKE (*Matter of factly*) It is indeed a sort of pilgrimage, for always we shall set forth to the honor of God and in the hope that young Robin will be even stronger at the end of our journey than he is now!

ROBIN *has been studying the letter through all this, saying the words over and nodding and smiling.* BROTHER MATTHEW *comes back with crutches for him and brings them down to him.*

ROBIN *shrieks with delight, grabs crutches, and rises, trying them out at once.*

He swings across stage more quickly than before. He is ecstatic.

GEOFFREY *has re-entered and he comes down and joins* ROBIN. *They cross from Left to Right, turn and race each other off down Left, laughing and shouting.*

The men are left on stage looking at one another with wonder. The monks cross themselves and look up to heaven with thanks and JOHN-GO-IN-THE-WYND *takes a few steps after the boys, watching them go as the curtain falls.*

CURTAIN

BROTHER MATTHEW   Here, Master Robin, are thine own crutches.

ROBIN   Oh, thank you, Brother Matthew. Oh! you've finished them for me. Thank you! Brother Matthew, thank you!

BROTHER LUKE (*Raising his arms*) Now praise our Lord's mercy! 'Twill be thine own crutches thou wilt wear.

GEOFFREY (*Calling*) Robin, Robin, wait for me!

ROBIN (*Shouts gaily*) Come along, Crookshanks!

STAGE DIRECTION

TIME   *One week later*

PLACE   *On the road*

There are sounds of oncoming storm—wind, etc. First part is played in front of curtain or on apron with darkened stage.

BROTHER LUKE *enters Left with* ROBIN, *carrying his crutches, on his back. He turns Left of Center and calls off Left to* JOHN.

ROBIN *holds on to* BROTHER LUKE *and pantomimes his fatigue, stretching and flexing his arm and leg muscles.* BROTHER LUKE *holds crutches.*

JOHN *enters from Left carrying cloaks and bundles of bedding, food, etc. He pauses at left of* BROTHER LUKE *and* ROBIN *and looks back off Left.*

ACT III

Scene I

NARRATOR   Robin, Brother Luke, and John-go-in-the-Wynd
have been on the road for a week. They have stayed in the
small inns that give the travelers a welcome rest along the
English country roads. But this day they have taken the
wrong fork in the road and now it is nightfall and there
is a storm approaching. The tired and hungry travelers
are looking for a place to spend the night.

BROTHER LUKE (*Calling*) Tie the horses securely, John. We
don't want to have to hunt them as we did this morning.

JOHN (*Calling from wings Left of stage*) I will, Brother
Luke, you may be sure.

BROTHER LUKE (*Grunts as he puts* ROBIN *on his feet*) There,
Master Robin, stretch thy legs a bit. It has been a long
hard ride this day.

ROBIN (*Tired*) It seems a week since we broke our fast this
morning.

BROTHER LUKE   It has indeed *been* a week since we left
St. Mark's.

JOHN   I don't think they will wander this night.

ROBIN *leads the way as* BROTHER LUKE *and* JOHN *pick up bundles and follow off Right, taking plenty of time, ad libbing about horses, etc. There are sounds of wind as they go off Right.*

They have made their way off Right slowly during preceding dialogue, each carrying bundles of clothing, cooking pots, blankets, and cloaks, etc. There is a pause covered by sounds of approaching storm and wind, etc. Allow time for characters to cross stage.

Curtain opens on dimly lit stage. ROBIN *re-enters from Left. (This is not essential but gives illusion of proceeding in one direction.)* ROBIN *is followed by* BROTHER LUKE *and* JOHN *from Left. There is a large hollow log, Left of Center, with the open end at a slight angle facing footlights.*

(Note: This can be made of a roll of wire or framework of lath covered with paper or canvas and painted to look like a log. This must be large enough for ROBIN *to hide in and heavy enough not to move when he crawls in and out. A black curtain may be used as backdrop and set within the interior which is necessary for fourth act. Scene may be spotted downstage if drapes are not available.)*

ROBIN   Kindly lend me a hand, Brother Luke, and set the crutches so I may walk awhile. (BROTHER LUKE *helps him adjust crutches*) Thank you.

BROTHER LUKE (*Wearily*) We've come a goodly way since morning. (*Sighs*) Would that we might have reached the White Swan before nightfall.

JOHN   Now, by my faith, I knew not which road to take.

BROTHER LUKE   Nor did I, never having taken this road before.

JOHN   Did that fellow not say the right fork?

BROTHER LUKE   My memory serves me ill. Whether he said the one or the other I know not.

STAGE DIRECTION

ROBIN *comes in from Left to Right of Center looking about,*
shivering.

The wind whistles and ROBIN *shivers, pulling his cloak*
about him.

JOHN *enters from Left and crosses* ROBIN *at Center, looking*
about.

JOHN *looks off Right and sets down bundles.* BROTHER LUKE
has entered from Left and crosses to them.

ROBIN *is moving about up Right and* JOHN *over to Left.*
JOHN *discovers log and peers inside.*

JOHN *turns to speak to the others who are below him.*

ROBIN (*Calling off*) What say you, Brother Luke? John? Does this seem a likely place?

BROTHER LUKE (*Offstage*) We're coming lad, we're coming.

JOHN We must have taken the wrong fork in the road. We've missed the Inn and night is nigh. Ahead lies a dark forest, and 'tis starting to rain. We shall seek shelter here by the road.

BROTHER LUKE (*Worried*) It is an ill thing for young Robin to sleep out in the damp, but if such be our fortune, then we must make the best of it. (*Setting down his bundles*)

JOHN (*To* BROTHER LUKE) Wild beasts do roam about and highwaymen lurk in the edge of the wood to leap out at passers-by. I say we stay here. (*He moves about as he talks*) I have flint and steel to make a fire.

BROTHER LUKE 'Tis naught for me to sleep in Mother Nature's arms. Many a night have I been grateful for the comfort of solid ground. (*He sits down on his bundles, moaning a bit with weariness*) And mayhap we can cover young Robin and keep him dry.

JOHN (*Pleased*) Why, here 'tis. The very thing. An ancient tree trunk fallen from age and hollowed with dry rot. It hath stood enough years to make it both wide and deep. We shall not be ill found after all.

ROBIN *moves over to look in log.*

JOHN *holds* ROBIN'S *crutches as he inspects hollow tree.*

ROBIN *has crawled into log, and* JOHN, *laying crutches down by log, goes over Right to pick up his bundle.*

JOHN *collects sticks and starts fire. He pantomimes making fire near the upstage end of the log with his flint and steel. A small collection of twigs can be left in upstage end of log for this purpose. Also, if practical, a small red electric bulb with switch can be placed by him for next scene.* BROTHER LUKE *crosses to log with robe to make bed for* ROBIN.

ROBIN *crawls out to let* BROTHER LUKE *make bed.*

ROBIN *stands and watches preparations.*

BROTHER LUKE *says prayers as curtain falls.* ROBIN *and* JOHN *kneel with him.*

> *Dim Out and CURTAIN as* ROBIN *Settles Down—*
> *A Short Interval to Denote Passage of Time*

ROBIN   Let me see! Let me see!

JOHN   Come, young master, let me help thee for I know thou'rt galled by the saddle, be it ever so soft.

BROTHER LUKE (*Undoing one of the bundles*) It is good that the fullers do shrink and pound this cloth, for it is well-nigh rainproof.

ROBIN   How snug and dry it is.

JOHN   I must get a fire going.

BROTHER LUKE   Come lad, I'll fix a bed for thee. Mayhap not so soft as one would be at the Inn but 'twill serve.

ROBIN   Oh! What fun to sleep out of doors. We'll roast apples. John will sing us a song, and you can tell us tales!

BROTHER LUKE (*As he makes up bed*) It is well to be safely housed after dark for thieves and roisterers do roam the country hereabout.

ROBIN   If my father were with us, we would have no fear of anyone.

BROTHER LUKE (*Crosses himself*) We shall have faith in the Father of us all.

A bit of music covers the interval with wind effect. The stage is dark except for small light indicating fire. Footlights come up to give enough light to see (firelight glows). There is a long pause and a stranger (a THIEF) *enters slowly on tiptoe from Left. He comes well in Center beyond log and sees the figures of* BROTHER LUKE *and* JOHN *lying asleep up Center, their heads to the fire and their feet extending downstage. He makes an elaborate pantomime gesture to someone off Left to follow, and putting his finger on his lips, warns him to be quiet. The* SECOND THIEF *enters on tiptoe. He trips and first man shushes him loudly—he picks up gesture in imitation. They are very roughly dressed and made up with dark, unshaven faces. The two are comic characters, tipsy and very clumsy. A cock crows.*

They creep up Right of Center on tiptoe toward the two sleeping men and take a good look. Then each shushing the other, they creep down to footlights making elaborate attempts to be quiet.

He places his hands above his ears to imitate a jackass.

FIRST THIEF *grabs him and shakes him to be quiet.*

Thieves speak in loud whispers. FIRST THIEF *looks about Right and Left to see if anyone sees them and thinks what to do next.* SECOND THIEF *nods and takes knife out of his waist band, licks his thumb and tries the edge.*

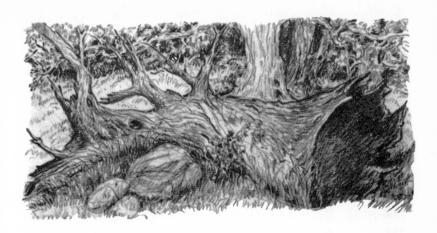

SECOND THIEF (*Frightened*) What's that? (*He starts off Left.* FIRST THIEF *grabs him*)

FIRST THIEF   Sh! (*Loud whisper*) 'Tis naught but a cock crowing. (*Looking about*) 'Tis near dawn.

FIRST THIEF (*Whispering loudly*) The big one snores like a braying jack.

SECOND THIEF (*Imitating snore*) Hee! Haw! Hee! Haw! Hee! Haw!

FIRST THIEF (*Hands over his mouth*) Ssh-s-ssh! I'll take the big one, and you take the friar. (*Loud whisper*) And be sure to get the money bag.

STAGE DIRECTION

During this dialogue, we see ROBIN *peering out from the log behind them. The two* THIEVES *turn Right and start tiptoeing up to sleeping men.* ROBIN *ducks back. As they cross above him,* ROBIN *comes out of log and slowly follows them on his knees. As they are about to pounce on the two sleepers,* ROBIN *shouts.*

All ad lib making a racket. The two THIEVES *are so startled that they start up—turn toward each other and bump together knocking one another down.* ROBIN *starts beating them with his crutch.* BROTHER LUKE *and* JOHN *spring up and they start clouting the two* THIEVES *and shouting—finally, after a mad scramble, driving them off Right.* ROBIN *manages to trip one of them with his crutch and gives him an extra whack as he goes.*

BLACKOUT

The three travelers have come back on stage and the lights have been coming up slowly, indicating morning. As the curtain rises, they are eating breakfast.

JOHN *imitates* ROBIN. *They go back to eating, enjoying the adventure now that it is past.*

ROBIN (*Shouting*) Robbers!

BROTHER LUKE (*Exclaiming*) What's that? Who? John, get them! Don't let them get away. (*Ad lib*)

JOHN Who? Ha? Wha-a-a?! (*Ad lib*)

ROBIN (*Hitting* THIEF) Take that! Varlet! And that! Stand and fight like a man!

◊

ROBIN (*Laughing*) I thought I would never stop laughing. They looked so funny not knowing who was after them.

BROTHER LUKE We were fortunate that they were so befuddled with ale they didn't know how many we were.

JOHN They must have thought Master Robin was a knight in armor and his crutch a lance. (*Laughing*) Ho! You varlet! Stand and fight like a man!

STAGE DIRECTION

A SHEPHERD *with crook enters from Left.* JOHN *jumps up ready to do battle again, but then subsides when he sees who it is.*

BROTHER LUKE *has gotten to his feet in greeting.*

SHEPHERD *comes over to join them.*

JOHN *hands* SHEPHERD *a cup, dipping first into bowl. He squats down beside them.*

ROBIN *is up and swinging his crutch at imaginary foe.* BROTHER LUKE *ducks and* JOHN *rolls out of way.*

All laugh, enjoying ROBIN's *good spirits.*

BROTHER LUKE   Ah, my fine fellow. Good morrow, come and breakfast with us.

SHEPHERD   I thank thee.

SHEPHERD   It is a cool morning indeed. Do you go to yon village? (*Gesturing off Right*)

ROBIN   Then we might have spent the night there instead of on the ground.

BROTHER LUKE   And spared ourselves the encounter with those villainous knaves to say naught of my aching bones.

ROBIN (*Intense*) Oh, but it was a great adventure! We routed them as my father routs the enemies of the King!

BROTHER LUKE   Mind how you swing that lance, Master Robin.

SHEPHERD   And how go the wars? Be they going well? Hast heard how 'tis with my Lord the King?

ROBIN (*Importantly*) It goes hardly, but it goes our way. I have had a letter saying that the King hopes for a peace by the Feast of Christmas. (ROBIN *assumes lordly stance*)

They rise and start breaking camp. Other people may now enter from Left and cross over Right carrying various things or pushing barrows or carts loaded with market goods.

CURTAIN CLOSES

As the scene changes from camp to road again, the same travelers and peasants cross in front of curtain from Left to Right, again giving illusion of moving in same direction. Music helps with this illusion—a rollicking country air would be suitable.

SHEPHERD   Peace? (*Ruefully*) Peace is what we all hope for. But, we find it seldom. For if 'tis not the Welsh 'tis the Scots. If 'tis neither one nor the other, then 'tis other neighbor against neighbor, or 'tis the lord of the manor against the peasants, begging thy pardon, young master.

ROBIN   'Tis naught. (*Shrugs deprecatingly*)

JOHN   Go you to the village? (*Gesturing off Right*)

SHEPHERD   No, I go to the forest of my lord's manor where wood for house fires may be gathered. We country folk may have such branches as can be gathered by hook or by crook from the standing trees of the lord's forest. (*Raises his crook pantomiming as if to hook branches*) Well I must be on my way. Good day! And thank 'ee for my breakfast. (SHEPHERD *nods and starts off Right.*)

ALL AD LIB   You're welcome. Good day! Good day!

BROTHER LUKE   And, we must gather our things and get on the road. We still have two or three days journey ere we reach Lindsay Castle.

TIME   *The next day*

PLACE   *A country town on the way to Lindsay where a Country Fair is taking place*

As curtain opens, there is music and folk dancing. There are booths at back of stage and Left. Upstage Right is a Punch and Judy Show. At conclusion of folk dance, acrobats and tumblers take over. A juggler comes on and does a turn. Two boys start scuffling, and encouraged by the crowd, they wrestle. Then the announcer calls everyone to the Punch and Judy Show.

ROBIN *and his companions have come on stage from down Left watching everything with great delight.*

JOHN *has been playing for the dancers and* BROTHER LUKE *crosses down Left to him.*

ROBIN *and the children all surround the Punch and Judy Show and watch performance.*

At conclusion of Punch and Judy Show there is a great shout of laughter, and BROTHER LUKE, JOHN, *and* ROBIN *start off Right at curtain.*

CURTAIN

ACT III

Scene II

(*Optional Scene*)

NARRATOR   The next day the wayfarers have traveled several miles when they come to a town with a Country Fair.

BROTHER LUKE   Hast seen enough, lad? It is a good way to the next hospice they tell me, and we have two or three days journey ahead of us. So come, my son.

ROBIN (*Pleading*) Let me see only the rest of the Punch and Judy, then I shall be willing, for never have I seen anything so funny.

BROTHER LUKE (*Shaking his finger admonishingly*) For that only, then we must be on our way.

TIME   *Two days later*

PLACE   *On the road to Lindsay*

This takes place in front of curtain. Other travelers move from Right to Left and from Left to Right.

ROBIN *and his companions enter from Left.* BROTHER LUKE *and* ROBIN *enter first.* ROBIN *is on his crutches.* BROTHER LUKE *turns to see how* ROBIN *is doing.*

BROTHER LUKE *turns as if to proceed, then turns back again to listen to* ROBIN *and speaks.*

JOHN *enters from Left*

ROBIN *looks down at his legs.*

JOHN *pats his shoulder in reassurance.*

ACT III

SCENE III

NARRATOR We are back on the road to Lindsay. The time is two days later.

BROTHER LUKE (*He stops Left of Center*) Now then, Master Robin, hast stretched thy legs enough? We must get on. Lindsay cannot be far.

ROBIN (*Nodding*) Let us be on our way, now that we are near to our journey's end. I wish to see my godfather, Sir Peter de Lindsay.

BROTHER LUKE How welcome the hearth and fire will be. Let us hope we shall be as welcome.

ROBIN (*To* JOHN) Think you he is a good man as my father says, John? How can he welcome me on crutches? Will he want me now to stay with him? (*Dolefully*) For how shall I be an esquire or even a page? I shall have no free hands for service.

JOHN (*Cheerfully*) It is well known in the country round about that he is a gracious master and a noble knight. His lady, too, is well loved for her goodness to the poor.

BROTHER LUKE *puts his arm around* ROBIN'S *shoulder.*

ROBIN *hands his crutches to* BROTHER LUKE *as they cross Right of Center.*

Suddenly ROBIN *sees something. He looks and points excitedly.*

All look at far corner Right rear of auditorium at one single spot.

BROTHER LUKE *looks to the heavens and blesses himself.*

JOHN *has set* ROBIN *down.* BROTHER LUKE *hands him his crutches.*

BROTHER LUKE *and* ROBIN *start off Right.*

BLACKOUT

Brother Luke   Fear not, my son, thou'lt find kind friends in thy new home.

John   Come, lad. (*Taking* Robin *on his shoulder*) We'll see what's beyond this next rise.

John (*As he crosses to Center*) We've had naught but one hill after another to climb since yesterday.

Brother Luke (*Moving with them*) Aye, we are all weary of this journey.

Robin   See there through the mist! Look! Look! There it is!

John   'Tis true! 'Tis as I hoped! We have arrived before sundown and can enter the castle before the gate is closed.

Brother Luke   Now thanks be to Him who guided us aright.

John   Lindsay it is, surely, for only Lindsay stands so, on a mound ringed with hills, like a pudding in a saucer.

Robin (*Laughing*) Like a pudding in a saucer, yes!

John   We've but to cross yon bridge, go up the hill and through the town gate and we are there! Beyond the town and castle lives my own mother.

Brother Luke   It is a happy end to our journey.

John (*Crossing back to Left*) I'll fetch the horses.

TIME   *One hour later*

PLACE   *Lindsay Hall*

This set can be the same interior as that used in first act with addition of wall decorations, banners, etc. Instead of bedroom furnishings we now are in a baronial hall. If it is practical, the doors and windows may be interchanged with those of first act. There should be a large fireplace at Right, chair above, small bench below fireplace and dais with chairs Left, table and benches up Center.

SIR PETER *is seated in chair up Right above fireplace.* LADY CONSTANCE, *with two boys and a little girl, is standing by* SIR PETER's *chair at Right above fireplace. Two pages,* DENIS *and* LIONEL, *are up Left.*

DENIS *crosses quickly down Left to usher in* BROTHER LUKE *and* ROBIN *followed by* JOHN *who crosses up to them Center.* SIR PETER *rises and crosses to Center.* SIR PETER *has left arm in sling or tucked into his jerkin and takes* ROBIN's *hand with his right.*

ACT IV

Scene I

NARRATOR   In a very short time our travelers reach the outer walls of Lindsay Castle and after being duly identified are shown into the presence of Sir Peter and his family. The scene is Lindsay Hall one hour later.

DENIS (*Crosses to left of* SIR PETER) Your Grace, Robin de Bureford and his servants await your pleasure.

SIR PETER   Show them in at once.

SIR PETER (*Kindly*) It is a true pleasure to welcome you into our household, Master Robin de Bureford.

ROBIN (*Bowing*) Thank you, Sir Peter.

SIR PETER *turns to* ROBIN.

LADY CONSTANCE *bows and* ALISON *curtseys.* ROBIN *bows and the boys shake hands with him.*

LADY CONSTANCE *crosses to* ROBIN *and brings him Right of Center putting her arms around him.*

LADY CONSTANCE *seats* ROBIN *on bench up Center below table.* SIR PETER, JOHN, *and* BROTHER LUKE *go up Left of Center.*

SIR PETER *crosses to* ROBIN, *places hand on his shoulder.*

ROBIN *looks up at* BROTHER LUKE *who smiles and nods.*

SIR PETER (*Drawing* ROBIN *to his right*) We are grateful to this good friar for his care of you. (BROTHER LUKE *bows, acknowledging* SIR PETER's *compliment*) And to John-go-in-the-Wynd, who is known to us. (*John bows also in response*) This is Lady Constance and our daughter Alison. And these are my two sons, Henry and Richard.

LADY CONSTANCE   Your father sent word of your illness and we have long awaited your coming, dear child. Now we are most happy that you have arrived safely.

ROBIN (*Ruefully*) I shall make a sorry page, my lady. But I can sing and I can read a little to while away the time (*He looks up to* SIR PETER) and I can pen letters for you, Sir.

SIR PETER   Each of us has his place in the world. If we cannot serve in one way, there is always another. If we do what we are able, a door always opens to something else.

LADY CONSTANCE (*Reassuringly*) Never fear child, you will be happy here with us.

ROBIN (*Eagerly*) I can sing a song or two.

LADY CONSTANCE (*Kindly*) And we'd like to hear you sing, perhaps after supper. (*She rises*) By your leave, good husband, I think our guests are fatigued and need to retire and refresh themselves.

SIR PETER *signals for* JOHN *to rise.* JOHN *crosses to* ROBIN, *and* SIR PETER *nods his approval.*

ROBIN *bows to* LADY CONSTANCE.

They exit, each page leading the way.

CURTAIN

sir peter   Of course, I should have thought. Denis! Lionel!
(*The two pages come forward*) Denis, Master Robin is to
be quartered next to your room in the keep. Lionel, take
Brother Luke to the room above the chapel.

john-go-in-the-wynd (*Dropping to his knee*) By your leave,
Sir, I would like to visit my old mother who lives in the
village of Tripheath, but I shall stay here awhile 'til my
young master finds his way about.

lady constance (*Helping* robin *up*) Go now, young Robin,
and rest awhile and we shall be together at supper.

robin   Thank you, my lady, and thank you, Sir Peter.

TIME   *Three days later*

PLACE   *Top of the keep—parapet of the castle*

Action is in front of curtain. A couple of portable steps may be used to indicate climbing up on parapet. JOHN *and* ROBIN *come on from Right.* JOHN *is helping* ROBIN *to find his steps.*

JOHN *looks out over audience as if to scan the landscape. Gestures from left to right.*

JOHN *points upstage and then points Left.*

They move around looking from Left rear of auditorium to Right rear and back again.

ACT IV

SCENE II

NARRATOR   Now that he has been well received, Robin finds everything about Lindsay exciting and interesting. The view from the top of the keep, where they go one morning a few days later, is breathtaking.

JOHN (*Ad lib*) Take care, Master Robin. There now!

ROBIN (*Looks out over audience toward Left rear*) Oh, how high we are! I can see for miles in every direction. Surely no enemy could attack without being seen by the watch from up here.

JOHN   Didst forget the fog? By night or under cover of the mist, a whole army could creep over hill and through forest without being seen. Lord Jocelyn to the west hath long coveted this domain and Sir Hugh Fitzhugh, to the north yonder who is cousin to Sir Peter, hath a quarrel with him.

ROBIN   But they could not take so strong a castle, surely.

JOHN   We can be starved out.

JOHN   Now that the castle is well known to thee and thou'rt started on making a minstrel's harp like mine, it is time for me to visit my old mother. Her cottage is there (*Pointing north offstage Left*) over the hill and into the next valley.

ROBIN *points to Left rear of auditorium.*

ROBIN *points back to rear of auditorium and gestures to Left of auditorium.*

JOHN *gestures down and then Left as if showing the way through town.*

JOHN *and* ROBIN *exit on the last line, laughing, off Right.*

CURTAIN

ROBIN Is it near to the village where yon church tower stands?

JOHN Aye, 'tis there this side of the church. (*Pointing and gesturing more to Left rear of auditorium*) A tidy bit of a house on the heath where she lives alone with her cat. There is a path all of the way. If thou'rt to call upon her, she would bake thee a bannock.

ROBIN (*Laughing*) Go you by that road I see leading up from the river here?

JOHN No, for 'tis a long way 'round by Letham Bridge. I go through the town and by the drover's road and across the ford beyond.

ROBIN I shall make your mother a visit when I am strong enough for such a long trip.

JOHN She'll welcome thee, lad. Now, dost know where to find me in case of need?

ROBIN Yes, 'tis over the path beyond the river, across yon field through the forest, then fording the stream and up another field through another wood and 'tis just there this side of the church in the village of Tripheath. (*Pointing out over audience as* JOHN *did*) A tidy bit of a house on the heath where she lives with her cat and if thou'rt there she'd bake thee a bannock. (ROBIN *mocks* JOHN)

JOHN (*Ad libs*) Now take heed where you place your crutches—watch thy step lad, etc.

TIME   *Evening of the same day*

PLACE   *Lindsay Hall*

SIR PETER *and* LADY CONSTANCE *with her ladies are seated with needlework at table up Center. Children are playing about.* DENIS *and* LIONEL *are fetching and carrying trays, mugs, plates, etc., up and offstage Right.* ROBIN *and* BROTHER LUKE *rise and come downstage.*

ROBIN *perks up as* BROTHER LUKE *encourages him.*

ROBIN *sits on bench and starts working on harp.*

ACT IV

SCENE III

NARRATOR   The family is finishing dinner in the Hall at Lindsay Castle. It is the evening of the same day. Robin and Brother Luke are very much at home.

ROBIN *(Plaintively as he moves down)* Think you it is really helping my legs to swim? I cannot straighten my back and can walk only as before, halfway bent over. *(Pause)* What think you, Brother Luke, shall I ever straighten?

BROTHER LUKE   I know not what to think about that. *(Slowly as he thinks about it)* God alone knows whether thou'lt straighten. I know not. *(Pauses)* But this I tell thee. A fine and beautiful life lies before thee because thou hast had the *will* to do it. Fret not, my son. *(Reassuring)* None of us is perfect. It is better to have crooked legs than a crooked spirit. We can only do the best we can with what we have. That, after all, is the measure of success.

ROBIN *(Seated)* Adam, the bowman, says I have a good arm for the bow and a keen eye for the mark. I can put an arrow up quite well for a beginner, he says.

BROTHER LUKE *looks more closely at* ROBIN'S *work.*

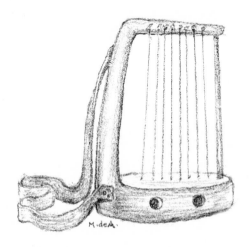

BROTHER LUKE *turns away as he sees* ROBIN *is satisfied.* ROBIN *is working on his harp.*

SIR PETER, *leaving the ladies to their needlework and small talk, comes downstage and joins* BROTHER LUKE *at Center.*

SIR PETER *goes over to window at Left and* BROTHER LUKE *joins him.* DENIS, *one of the pages, comes down to* ROBIN.

BROTHER LUKE   And how goes the woodworking?

ROBIN (*Picking up harp, proudly*) John has shown me how to shape the base. See, (*Showing him*) it is to be almost like his but is to have my own mark. His is plain. Mine shall have tracery. John showed me how to shape the post. It is of maple, well seasoned and beautifully marked. Adam, the bowman, is drying deergut for me to make the strings.

BROTHER LUKE (*Happily*) Thou'rt becoming a true craftsman. And wilt be able to play the harp when 'tis done?

ROBIN (*Happily*) Already I can pick part of the tune "Ca' the Yaws" and can sing it as well. It is sad, but pleasant to hear. (*Confidentially*) When I learn it all, I shall sing it for Lady Constance. (*Wistfully*) And when I see my mother again I shall sing it for her. (*He pauses thoughtfully*) Think you my mother will know me when she sees me thus? (*Indicating his crippled legs*)

BROTHER LUKE (*Comforting him*) Thy mother will know and love thee always, my son. Whether thou art bent or straight, well or ill, knight or clerk, lord or minstrel.

SIR PETER (*Worriedly*) I know not what to think of the mist. It gives cause for anxiety that it lasts so long.

BROTHER LUKE (*Alarmed*) Think you the Welsh will attack?

SIR PETER (*Regretfully*) Would that John-go-in-the-Wynd were here to send for help. I gave him leave to visit his mother only this morning.

A bloodcurdling scream is heard off Left. There are shouts back and forth. All on stage are startled and shaken by this sound from afar.

SIR PETER *and* BROTHER LUKE *look out of window off Left anxiously.* ROBIN *stays seated with* DENIS *by him.*

Again there are sounds of shouting and running offstage Left.

SIR PETER *and* BROTHER LUKE *come down as* ADAM, *the bowman, runs in from down Left, breathless.*

SIR PETER *reaches for his sword which hangs on the wall.* ADAM *moves with* SIR PETER *as he girds himself.*

DENIS (*Confidentially*) There be a treacherous cloud over the whole valley.

ROBIN (*Concerned*) Will there be danger in it, think you?

DENIS Aye, danger enough! (*Gravely*) The Welsh yonder long have wanted this castle, for it be strong. Now with fog to help and so few to guard the walls, there is chance they might get it, God forbid.

ROBIN (*Somewhat fearfully*) If only my father would come with his men, we would be safe. (*Bragging*) He is the strongest knight in the King's bodyguard and Elfred, the Dane, is his finest bowman. Elfred can shoot out the eyes of an owl at two hundred paces. (*Woefully*) But, neither Elfred nor my father is here.

ADAM Your Lordship! (*Excited, bobs his head*) We are attacked. The Welsh are hammering at the town gate! They have slain the watch by creeping close to the wall in the fog! They waited for him to turn, then put an arrow in his back!

SIR PETER 'Tis come then. (*Deeply concerned*) What strength are they? Is it known?

LADY CONSTANCE *ad libs giving orders to ladies to fetch bedding, etc.*

The pages exit up Right. The women and girls exit up Right or down Right. The two little boys excitedly gather around SIR PETER.

SIR PETER *exits down Left.* ROBIN *draws boys to him.*

BLACKOUT

CURTAIN

ADAM (*Still breathless*) It is hard to say. They make a great noise about the walls, but naught can be seen for the fog. They have built fires under the south gate and torches glow on all sides, so I fear we are surrounded.

SIR PETER (*Commanding them*) Gather every man not armed into the inner bailey where they will be provided with longbows and arrows! You, my dear wife, gather all the women and children here! Have them bring clothing and pallets! Here, at least, we have water in the well and 'tis a strong fortress!

LADY CONSTANCE (*She bobs curtsey*) Yes, my husband. Lionel, Denis! Go you to the kitchen and bring what food and drink you can find here to the great hall.

ROBIN (*Rises*) What can I do, Sir Peter?

SIR PETER You can mind the little boys and keep them close to you. Come Adam, Brother Luke!

TIME   *One week later*

PLACE   *Lindsay Hall*

The curtain opens on the same scene. ROBIN *is seated on his bench down Right. The little boys are playing with blocks of wood and shavings at* ROBIN'S *feet. The women and girls are clustered around the table up Center, sewing, weaving, etc. The little girls are playing with dolls* ROBIN *has made for them.*

LADY CONSTANCE *enters from up Right with one of her ladies and crosses down to Left of Center. Children cluster around her showing their gifts.*

LADY CONSTANCE *listens to the children, turns, and smiles to* ROBIN. *She speaks to* LADY MARGARET.

ACT IV

SCENE IV

NARRATOR   The fog holds for days. The Welsh have breached the walls of the town and most of the townspeople have taken refuge in the castle, still protected by the moat and inner walls. It is now one week later. Inside the castle in the Great Hall, the women keep busy and Robin attempts to entertain the small children with his stories and songs.

FIRST LITTLE BOY   Mother, see what Robin has given me!

LADY CONSTANCE   Why, that is a lovely boat.

LITTLE GIRL   And see the doll Robin made for me!

LADY CONSTANCE   He is very good to you children.

LADY CONSTANCE   (*Worriedly*) The food is dwindling day by day. We've not had a chance to replenish it this long week of the siege.

LADY MARGARET   (*Concerned*) There is a good supply of flour, my lady, but the mutton is still on four legs and scattered over the hills outside the town.

LADY CONSTANCE   What of the supply of salt fish? Are any left?

STAGE DIRECTION

Both ladies move up Left as they talk. The little boys rise and follow them, begging for food.

DENIS *has come down to* ROBIN'S *left carrying pitcher of water and has been listening to conversation between* LADY CONSTANCE *and* LADY MARGARET. *He leans over and whispers in* ROBIN'S *ear.*

ROBIN *looks up at* DENIS *with worried expression.*

DENIS *continues to speak in low voice so that women do not hear.*

DENIS *exits off Left. The ladies have been conferring up Left and cross to up Right as they speak.*

LADY MARGARET *exits off up Right.*

BROTHER LUKE *enters from down Right and crosses to* ROBIN.

LADY MARGARET   Yes, my lady, but it too is dwindling.

LADY CONSTANCE   We've so many to feed. (*Pauses to pick up sewing, lays it down again*) Thanks be to God we have a good water supply.

DENIS (*Confidentially*) There is scarce a foot of water in the well. Just now as I drew the water to fill this ewer, the cook told me.

ROBIN   What shall we do? Sir Peter has taken to his bed with a chill suffered last night when he led the men against that Welsh raiding party trying to scale the east wall.

DENIS   Where is Brother Luke?

ROBIN   With Sir Peter I warrant, planning our defenses for this night.

DENIS   Perhaps we should tell Lady Constance.

ROBIN   No, better to fetch Adam Bowyer and he can tell us what to do.

LADY CONSTANCE   I must see to Sir Peter's comfort. Please to take my instructions to the kitchen.

LADY MARGARET   Yes, my lady.

BROTHER LUKE (*Briskly*) Well, lad, hast been busy I see.

STAGE DIRECTION

ROBIN *is very much concerned and worried.*

ADAM *enters from down Left and crosses to Center, speaking to* BROTHER LUKE.

ADAM *stands thinking for a moment and the others watch him.*

ROBIN *rises.*

ROBIN   How fares Sir Peter?

BROTHER LUKE   (*Reassuringly*) He will be well enough to join us at supper, I warrant.

ADAM   How is this? Denis tells me that the water is low in the well!

BROTHER LUKE   (*Shaking head, as if shocked*) I know it not! (*To* DENIS) Does Sir Peter know of this?

DENIS   (*Shaking head*) I have not told him. Nor have I told her ladyship.

ADAM   (*Puzzling the problem*) It has always been known as a good well . . . Tell not her ladyship.

BROTHER LUKE   What are we to do?

ADAM   Send the word around that the water must be used sparingly or 'twill not last the week out. Even for drinking.

BROTHER LUKE   I will see to it. (*Exits up Right*)

ADAM   (*Decisively*) Someone must go for help or we shall be forced to surrender the castle! (*Pause*) It might be that Sir Hugh Fitzhugh would come to our aid for he, too, is in danger from the Welsh if they break our defenses. But whom shall we spare? All are needed at their posts. (*Pause*)

ROBIN   (*Eagerly*) Let me go! I can go out the small door at the north whilst it is early morning! No one will suspect me! They'll think me a poor shepherd. I shall borrow a smock from William, the Farrier's son, and if I am

ROBIN *must demonstrate his strength and confidence by his movements.*

ADAM *exits down Left.*

LADY CONSTANCE *and* LADY MARGARET *enter from down Right, cross to Center and up .to table.* DENIS *stops talking when women approach.* LADY CONSTANCE *speaks as she crosses.*

DENIS *and* ROBIN *exchange looks.*

DENIS *exits down Right.* ROBIN *sitting at his bench starts gathering his things together.*

BLACKOUT

seen, I shall appear stupid. We shall keep it secret, for if Sir Peter were to find out my plan he would forbid me to go, not knowing how strong I am.

ADAM   But thou are only a lad and art cumbered with crutches as well. And how wilt thou cross the river? The bridge is well guarded at both ends.

ROBIN   I shall go well, never fear. I have it all in my head how it shall be done. I shall find John-go-in-the-Wynd at his mother's cottage in Tripheath Village. John shall set forth from there for Sir Hugh and his men. Now, let us plan. (*Taking charge*) First I want you, Denis, to bring me a smock and some rags to wrap about my legs. Then, see you, find me a hood that is worn and faded. Besides, I shall need long leather thongs to tie the crutches to my back, for I shall swim the river.

ADAM   (*Wonderingly*) Thou art a brave lad indeed. God speed you.

DENIS   (*Anxiously*) Fear you not the soldiery? Will you not fall down the steep bank? 'Tis a far distance to the bottom of the ravine and . . .

LADY CONSTANCE   How fortunate we are that there is plenty of water. Sir Peter says that our well has never failed.

ROBIN   (*In a loud whisper to* DENIS) Fetch the clothes I shall need.

TIME   *Early next morning*

PLACE   *Outside walls of Lindsay Castle*

Action takes place in front of curtain. BROTHER LUKE *and* ROBIN *enter from Right.*

BROTHER LUKE *bundles hood around* ROBIN'S *head and neck as if loathe to let him go.*

ROBIN *is shaking somewhat, more from eagerness than fear*

They withdraw off Right.

The SENTRY *comes in from Left, crosses to Center and turns back and off Left again, his steps receding.*

BROTHER LUKE *and* ROBIN *enter again from Right.*

BROTHER LUKE *turns* ROBIN *to him for a last look and makes sign of the cross over him.*

ACT IV

Scene V

NARRATOR   It is early next morning just before dawn, outside the walls of Lindsay Castle

BROTHER LUKE   Art fearful, my son?

ROBIN   Not truly, though 'tis weird in the fog.

BROTHER LUKE   (*Looking up*) Aye, 'tis an eerie feeling to be out in the cheerless dawn. Hark! I hear the Welsh sentry.

BROTHER LUKE   We can count the paces and tell how far away he is. One, two, three, four, (*They counted forty paces*) Now! Benedicite!

ROBIN *turns and starts across Left.* BROTHER LUKE *watches him go, then turns back and exits off Right.*
ROBIN *makes his way slowly across stage. Just as he is about to exit, we hear the* SENTRY

ROBIN *turns as if to run back. As* SENTRY *enters from Left,* ROBIN *faces him.*

SENTRY *takes a long look at him.*

ROBIN *controls himself.*

SENTRY *reaches for* ROBIN'S *arm, but* ROBIN *circles around him, going Left stage.*

ROBIN *tries to appear stupid, and bobbing his thanks he exits Left followed by* SENTRY.

BLACKOUT

SENTRY (*Shouting off Left*) Who goes there?

ROBIN (*Stammering*) 'Tis but I, Robin.

SENTRY (*Sternly*) Robin who?

ROBIN (*Shaking with fright*) Robin Crookshank, some call me.

SENTRY   Aah, thou'rt but a shepherd boy, then.

ROBIN   Aye! (*Relieved, but still shaking*)

SENTRY (*Gently*) Art thou cold? Come warm thyself by the fire.

ROBIN   No-o-o-o, thank 'ee.

SENTRY (*Reassuring*) Be not frightened. We'll not hurt thee.

ROBIN   Nay, 'tis not far to the cottage. Thank 'ee, thank 'ee.

TIME *One hour later, the same day*

PLACE *The cottage of* JOHN-GO-IN-THE-WYND

Lights come up in front of curtain. JOHN *is at Right stage picking up firewood. He is bareheaded.* ROBIN *enters from Left and speaks.*

ROBIN *shows fatigue, almost falling.* JOHN *runs to him.*

JOHN *picks up* ROBIN *and carries him off Right.*

The curtain opens and we are in the cottage. Note: This can be a simple two-flat set, L-shaped, within the larger interior lit by one spot on simulated fireplace.

JOHN, *entering from Right, lays* ROBIN *down and starts rubbing his arms and legs.* JOHN's *old mother steps down to help.* ROBIN *comes to after a moment.*

ACT IV

Scene VI

NARRATOR   Robin manages to escape the sentry, and after a long and difficult journey down the steep bank to the bottom of the ravine and a frigid swim across the river, he finds what he seeks, following John's directions, the cottage of John-go-in-the-Wynd. It is about one hour later.

ROBIN (*Calling*) John-go-in-the-Wynd!

JOHN   Master Robin! What's amiss? How cam'st thou here? Thou'rt soaking wet and cold as yesterday's porridge! Didst fall in the river?

ROBIN   No, I swam across.

JOHN   Ah, thou'rt a brave lad.

JOHN *is already putting on his hood and jerkin as he listens to* ROBIN.

JOHN *crosses stage, very excited, and exits off Left.*

ROBIN *is very relieved.* OLD WOMAN *nods and smiles and crosses up to fireplace.*

BLACKOUT
to indicate passage of time

ROBIN (*Desperately*) The castle is in danger! The Welsh have taken the town and are at the gates of the outer bailey! The food is giving out. The water is low in the well. You must get help from Sir Hugh! You must get it soon!

JOHN (*Hurriedly*) But how cam'st thou here? How did'st escape the sentry? Know'st what force the Welsh have?

ROBIN   No, the fog has kept us from seeing, but whenever we tried to make a sally into the town, we were forced back.

JOHN   I shall be gone straight away. Stay thou here for safety and to rest!

OLD WOMAN (*Coming to* ROBIN *and taking off his hood*) Come, now, thou'lt be famished with hunger. I'll bake thee a bannock.

ROBIN (*Laughing*) That sounds good. John told me you were a good cook.

TIME   *Late afternoon the same day*

PLACE   *The same cottage scene with* ROBIN *sleeping*

As lights come up, ROBIN *rises up from sleeping position and* JOHN *enters from Left.*

ROBIN *is up on his crutches almost jumping with joy.*

JOHN *pantomimes, patting his hollow stomach.*

NARRATOR   It is late in the afternoon of the same day.

ROBIN *(Wonderingly)* Did you not go then?

JOHN *(Proudly)* Gone and back again!

ROBIN *(Eagerly)* Did you find help with Sir Hugh?

JOHN   Yes, and greatest news of all, Sir Hugh has received word that the King, his knights and men-at-arms
are within an hour's ride and Sir Hugh has sent a messenger to tell his Majesty of our peril. Already, my lord Hugh
Fitzhugh is well on his way with a large force of foot
soldiers, and a company of lancers go by the drovers' road,
one company by way through wood and field and the
other going around to attack from the other side of the
town by way of Letham Bridge. It hath been agreed
that we shall give the signal from the bell tower of the
church. There are no better bowmen in England. The siege
will be lifted. Thou'lt see.

ROBIN *(Shouting)* I want to see it! I want to see it all!

JOHN   See it thou shalt! Now, Mother, serve forth yon
porridge, for I have not broken my fast this day.

OLD WOMAN *serves two bowls from pot at fireplace. They pantomime eating quickly.* JOHN *gathers up his harp, puts knife in belt, etc.*

ROBIN *sags a bit on his crutches as he thinks of the journey he must make.*

JOHN *fastens crutches to his side and harp about his neck.*

JOHN *embraces his mother and lifts* ROBIN *up on shoulder.*

Ad lib. JOHN *and* ROBIN *exit off Right.*

BLACKOUT

CURTAIN

JOHN   I am no warrior. I am but a messenger and a minstrel. But who knows, I might find myself close to the enemy. Closer than I would like.

ROBIN   Think you I can go so far again this day?

JOHN (*Bragging*) Thou hast no need to think of that! I can carry thee right well as the good friar did. The harp and the crutches we shall strap on so they will not cumber us.

JOHN   Soon thou'lt be carrying thy own harp, God willing. Fare thee well, old Mother. Up now, young master!

ROBIN (*Laughing, as they go off*) How shall we go?

JOHN   I know a path through the forest to the southeast. We shall creep along the river under cover of reeds and willows.

STAGE DIRECTION

TIME *About two hours later*

TIME   *About two hours later*

PLACE   *Parapet of Lindsay Castle*

Action takes place in front of curtain as before. Use steps to indicate climbing up on parapet from Right. A dim spot lights up stage Right.

JOHN *enters first carrying* ROBIN'S *crutches, looking back encouragingly.*

JOHN *hands crutches back to* ROBIN.

ROBIN *looks up to see where the moon is now.*

126

ACT IV

SCENE VII

NARRATOR   It is two hours later in the same day. Robin and
John have reached Lindsay Castle by carefully screening
themselves behind hedges and low banks of earth. They
reach a place in the wall under the shoemaker's cottage
where John signals by playing a tune on his harp. A
chair is let down from a window and our heroes are lifted
inside the castle walls. We are now again on the parapet
of the castle.

JOHN   Give me thy crutches. (*Gives* ROBIN *a hand*) Can'st
thou climb all right?

ROBIN (*Breathlessly*) I can do it.

JOHN (*Looking over the town*) For aught I know, Sir Hugh
has surrounded the town. We agreed to wait an hour after
curfew when the moon will be overhead.

ROBIN   How can you tell when it has been an hour?

JOHN (*Looking out, excited*) By the feel of it. It's almost
time. See there! Across the river! Something is moving!
It must be Sir Hugh's men?

*A great bell sounds offstage—*BONG! BONG! BONGGGG!
Both JOHN *and* ROBIN *cover their ears.* ROBIN *shakes his head as if to clear it, as sound fades.*

There are sounds of shouting and cheering offstage. Din of battle increases throughout scene.

They look off and to far Left. JOHN *and* ROBIN *must each look at the same spot.*

As fighting comes closer, sounds offstage become louder.

Shouting to be heard above sounds offstage, JOHN *clasps* ROBIN *and jumps up and down, each hugging the other.*

Sounds become louder and louder as the fight comes closer.

JOHN *lifts* ROBIN *up on his shoulder and dances about with joy. There is much loud cheering offstage.*

BLACKOUT

robin (*Catching the fever of excitement from* john) I do see something shining in the moonlight . . .

john (*After a pause*) . . . Now, it is time for the alarm!

robin What's to be seen? Are they moving?

john Yes, it is as if the whole hillside is moving! See the arrows fly!

robin (*Almost shrieking*) WHERE? WHERE? SHOW ME?

john There, see! A very hail of arrows by Letham Bridge!

robin I see! I see! Look, the sentries fall! There is one falling off the wall of the town.

john Now they are rushing across the bridge! See how they come with pikes lowered! They're across and at the town gate!

robin (*Shrieking*) Look! Look yonder! Another company of knights and men-at-arms! It is the King and my father!

john By my faith! We will win this day. It is the King, surely. See how they stream down the hillside toward the town! It is a rout. We have won! We have won!

john Now thou'lt be carried on my shoulder so, for thou are the hero of this victory!

robin (*Shouting*) Hurrah! Hurrah! We've won! We've won!

STAGE DIRECTION

TIME   *A few minutes later*

PLACE   *Lindsay Hall*

Noise of victory, shouting, bells, etc. are heard offstage. As curtain rises SIR JOHN *and* BROTHER LUKE *enter from up Right and cross to window Left.* ADAM *enters from down Left carrying bow, and* SIR PETER *carrying sword crosses to Center, anticipating* ADAM'S *entrance.* BROTHER LUKE *stays up by window Left.* ADAM *crosses to* SIR PETER.

BROTHER LUKE *takes step or two down.* ROBIN *and* JOHN *enter from down Right, followed by* DENIS *and* LIONEL. *They hear what* ADAM *is saying.*

All are talking and shouting at once "A victory," "We've done it," "The Welsh are routed." BROTHER LUKE *crosses to* ROBIN *and embraces him.*

ROBIN *is too excited to stand still. He crosses to* SIR PETER.

ROBIN *turns back to* BROTHER LUKE *who stands with* JOHN *Right of Center.* ROBIN *is almost in tears with joy. He crosses to window Left in his excitement to see, then crosses back to* SIR PETER.

SIR PETER *places hand on* ROBIN'S *head. He glances at* BROTHER LUKE *and back to* ROBIN.

ACT IV

SCENE VIII

NARRATOR   We are in the Hall of Lindsay Castle, immediately following the battle.

ADAM   Sir Peter! (*Bobs his head*) We've won! We've won! Sir Hugh has routed the enemy and *another* company of knights has joined the battle! It is a complete victory!

ROBIN (*Crosses to Center*) It is true! It is true!

BROTHER LUKE   Master Robin!

ROBIN   The Scottish wars are over. The King is coming with my father. My father is alive! There are ladies, too. I wonder. Could it be that my lady mother is with them!

SIR PETER   Well, well, young sir. I hear you have done a great and heroic deed. (*Pause*) Did you not go to fetch John-go-in-the-Wynd?

JOHN (*Proudly*) Indeed, he did, Sir.

ROBIN *is too excited to stand still. He wants to go to window and watch.*

ROBIN *squirms uncomfortably, and as* SIR PETER *turns to* JOHN, *he escapes crossing up to window.*

JOHN *kneels and kisses* SIR PETER'S *hand.* SIR PETER *raises him up.*

ROBIN *crosses down to* SIR PETER *from window.*

SIR PETER *roars with laughter at* ROBIN'S *excitement.*

ROBIN *moves as fast as he can up to window again.*

ADAM *bobs head and exits down Left.*

ROBIN *moves back to* SIR PETER *again, still excited, hopping around in his agitation.*

SIR PETER (*To* JOHN) And did you not go to fetch Sir Hugh to tell him of our dire need?

JOHN (*Bows head*) I did only my duty. But Master Robin brought me word. If he had not, I'd not have known of thy peril.

SIR PETER (*Holding on to* ROBIN) Now, before God and this company, I do hail thee conqueror and true son of thy noble father, and you, John-go-in-the-Wynd (*Turning to him*) thou shalt be given a holding of land and a flock of forty sheep for yourself and your heirs from this time forth.

ROBIN (*Excitedly*) Shall I go to the gate to be there when they enter, think you, Sir Peter?

SIR PETER Do what seems best. Go stand beside Alan-at-Gate or stay you here by my side. I know what a fever of excitement is in thy bones, but do what you most want to do.

SIR PETER (*To* ADAM) Adam, see that the men are drawn up to greet the King.

ROBIN If I stand beside you, my lord, they will surely know it is I. If they see me in the courtyard, they may think I am but one of the stable boys. I shall stay here!

DENIS *bobs his head and exits up Right.*
LIONEL *exits down Right.*
JOHN *looks ruefully at his soiled jerkin.*
SIR PETER *laughs and touches* ROBIN'S *head.*
Each one bows to SIR PETER.

BROTHER LUKE, ROBIN, *and* JOHN *exit down Right.*

SIR PETER *takes step over to window.* LADY CONSTANCE, MISTRESS ALISON, *and* LADY MARGARET *enter up Right, followed by* DENIS *and* LIONEL.

LIONEL *exits up Right.*
SIR PETER *has crossed over to window Left, looking off.*

SIR PETER Denis, go you to find your mistress. Lionel, fetch my two sons and see that they are presentable. Robin, betake you to your chamber and put on a clean jerkin and hose. John too. Your doublets at least should be clean, and comb the burrs out of your hair. Haste, now, both of you. The King and your father will soon arrive.

BROTHER LUKE Much hath happened in this one day. I should like to hear how this journey went. By thy look, Robin, thou hast fared well except for needing of a good wash.

LADY CONSTANCE (*As she enters*) What is happening? Is the battle over?

SIR PETER (*Turning to her, triumphantly*) My Lady, we have won the day! Thanks be to God and Sir Hugh, my cousin. (*Pause*) We have royal visitors. The King and Queen have arrived with Sir John de Bureford and his whole company.

LADY CONSTANCE (*Flabbergasted by all the excitement*) The King and Queen! By my faith! The house is in woeful disorder. (*Decisively*) Well, we shall have to make the best of it. Lionel, go you to the kitchen. Have the cooks send into the town at once to fetch what food they may find.

The ladies exit up Right. ADAM *enters down Left.*

ADAM *exits.*
There is a terrific clamor offstage. Horses and men in armor, shouts offstage "Halt!" "Dismount!" etc.

BROTHER LUKE *re-enters from down Right (carries* ROBIN'S *harp).*

LADY CONSTANCE *and others of household pour in from Right and arrange themselves to receive the* KING. ADAM *enters from down Left, ushering in the* KING, *followed by* QUEEN *and* SIR JOHN, LADY MAUD, *and company.*

KING *and* QUEEN *cross to Center stage followed by* SIR JOHN *and* LADY MAUD.

SIR PETER *kneels Right of Center.*

BROTHER LUKE *stands behind him bowing his head.*

Whole household makes obeisance.

The KING *raises him and takes his hand.*

LADY CONSTANCE   Lady Margaret, please to take Mistress Alison to her room and find her a clean gown. I, too, shall attire myself in suitable raiment.

ADAM   The men are ready, Sir. Will't come to the court-yard to review them?

SIR PETER   I haven't quite recovered from the chill. I shall await our guests here. Do you bid them welcome and guide his Majesty and the company here.

ADAM   Aye, Sir, I shall do my best, Sir.

BROTHER LUKE   Sir Peter, they have arrived!

SIR PETER   Where is Master Robin?

BROTHER LUKE   He'll be here in a moment, Your Grace.

ADAM *(Announcing)* Their Majesties, The King and Queen of England and France.

SIR PETER   Your Majesty.

The KING *crosses to* LADY CONSTANCE *and raises her.*

Others rise with LADY CONSTANCE. *The* KING *brings* LADY CONSTANCE *across to Center where he presents her to* QUEEN.

LADY CONSTANCE
QUEEN *(Ad lib, each saying name of other:* "LADY CONSTANCE," "YOUR MAJESTY," *etc.)*

LADY CONSTANCE *curtsies as do all the household—the men bow. The* QUEEN *graciously acknowledges* LADY CONSTANCE.

At this point after greetings have been exchanged, ROBIN *enters down Right followed by* JOHN-GO-IN-THE-WYND. *There is a pause while all look his way. He takes a step or two into the Right of Center.* LADY MAUD *rushes to him, followed by* SIR JOHN. *Others turn up and to Left;* SIR PETER *whispers in* KING'S *ear of* ROBIN'S *exploits.*

She holds him close. ROBIN *drops his crutches to return his mother's embrace.* SIR JOHN, *deeply moved though he laughs, picks up the crutches, crossing in back of and to right of* ROBIN *and* LADY MAUD. *He shows his emotion by holding crutches against his breast and bowing head slightly as mother and son embrace.*

SIR JOHN *embraces* ROBIN *and then holds him at arms length.*

SIR JOHN *hugs* ROBIN *again.* SIR PETER *has guided the* KING *and* QUEEN *to the dais at Left.*

KING   Sir Peter! Ah, my comrade-in-arms. It is good to see you have recovered from your wounds suffered in our service. (*Turns to* LADY CONSTANCE) Your Ladyship!

LADY MAUD   Robin, my Robin.

SIR JOHN   (*Gently turns* ROBIN *to him. Hands crutches to* LADY MAUD) He is my son too.

SIR JOHN   You have grown. Your eyes no longer outrace your chin as do a child's. You've now the look of a youth!

SIR PETER *crosses to group Right of Center.*

SIR JOHN *and* LADY MAUD *step aside after* LADY MAUD *gives* ROBIN *his crutches, holding positions at Right of Center, and* ROBIN *crosses to Center.*

SIR PETER *places hand on* ROBIN'S *shoulder.*

ROBIN *crosses to dais.*

ROBIN *kneels, supporting himself with one crutch.* SIR PETER *takes the other.*

KING *raises* ROBIN *to his feet and* SIR PETER *hands him second crutch. Everyone cheers and claps hands.*

sir peter   Shall we present our young hero to his King?

robin   (*Joyfully*) If you please, Sir!

sir peter   (*Proudly*) Your Majesty, may I present Robin de Bureford, son of Sir John de Bureford, and our squire and page, who so nobly swam the river to carry news of the invasion to our minstrel and messenger, John-go-in-the-Wynd.

king   Come forward, Robin de Bureford. Can you kneel, my son?

robin   I can for a little time, Sire.

king   Robin, son of Sir John de Bureford, it hath been told to us what service you have done for the lord of this castle and me, King of the whole realm of England and France. You are a true son of a noble father. Though but a youth, you have shown courage a man might be proud to call his own. (*Standing, the* king *takes necklace from his own shoulders and places it around* robin's *neck*) This shall be a token of our high regard and with it go our grateful thanks. Rise, young Robin de Bureford.

BROTHER LUKE *brings over little stool with harp to Center.*

ROBIN *sits and sings (possibly song found on page 145).*

After applause has died down, SIR JOHN *and* LADY MAUD *cross to* ROBIN *at Center.* SIR JOHN *lifts him up and embraces him.* ROBIN *looks up at him as he speaks.*

ROBIN *laughs with relief and turns and hugs his mother.* LADY MAUD *holds him in her arms.*

ROBIN *crosses to* BROTHER LUKE *who has come down to them.*

EVERYONE Hurrah for Sir Robin de Bureford! etc. Long live Sir Robin! etc. (*Ad lib*)

ROBIN Sir, I thank you for this great honor and may I sing you a song?

KING By all means! A song!

EVERYONE A song! A song! (*Laughter, clapping, etc. Ad lib*)

ROBIN Sir, mind you not that I must go thus, bent over and with these crutches to help me walk?

SIR JOHN (*Gravely*) The courage you have shown, the craftsmanship proven by the harp and the spirit in your singing all make so bright a light that I cannot see whether or no your legs are misshapen.

LADY MAUD As for me, what a comfort it will be to know that wars will never claim you. We shall all go home to London. Brother Luke shall come with us to be your tutor, if he will.

ROBIN What think you, Brother Luke?

BROTHER LUKE I think the Lord smiles on you, Master Robin. Thou art safe with all thy loved ones and thou hast found the door in thy wall.

STAGE DIRECTION

Reprise on song. All on stage join in.

CURTAIN

4/4 time

Come to the manger bed, See the light a-round his head.

Child of God, whom we adore, Child of God, whom we adore.

END

PROPERTY PLOT

Act I

BOWL AND SPOON	DAME ELLEN
BASKET OF FOOD, SPOON, FORK, ETC.	BRO. LUKE
BOWL, PITCHER AND TOWEL	BRO. LUKE
CHEST WITH ROBIN'S CLOTHES, CLOAK WITH HOOD AND BUNDLE TO CARRY	BRO. LUKE

Act II

KNIFE AND WOOD FOR BOAT	ROBIN
TOOLS ON CARPENTER'S BENCH, RUBBING STONE, ETC.	BRO. MATTHEW
BOWL AND SPOON	BRO. LUKE
BITS OF CLOTH WITH YARN AND RIBBON	BRO. LUKE
CRUTCHES	GEOFFREY
WOOD FOR CROSS (ONE PIECE BREAK-AWAY)	ROBIN

PROPERTY PLOT Acts II, III, IV

CRUTCHES	ROBIN
PROP CHISEL	ROBIN
SMALL SCROLLS, INK POT, QUILL PEN	BRO. LUKE
TWO STICKS TO CARRY ROBIN'S SHIRT	TWO CHILDREN
LARGE SCROLL IN CART	BRO. LUKE
SMALL HARP	JOHN-GO-IN-THE-WYND
SMALL SCROLL	JOHN-GO-IN-THE-WYND

Act III

CRUTCHES	ROBIN
BLANKETS, CLOAKS, BUNDLES, POTS, BOWLS, CUPS	JOHN-GO-IN-THE-WYND
SMALL TWIGS, FLINT AND STEEL	JOHN-GO-IN-THE-WYND
PROP FIRE	
KNIFE	FIRST THIEF
MONEY BAG	BRO. LUKE
SHEPHERD'S CROOK	SHEPHERD
BUNDLES, CARTS, MARKET GOODS, ETC.	COUNTRY FOLK

Act IV

CRUTCHES	ROBIN
HARP	JOHN-GO-IN-THE-WYND
TABLEWARE, TRAYS, MUGS, PLATES, ETC.	LIONEL AND DENIS

148

PARTIALLY ASSEMBLED HARP	ROBIN
NEEDLEWORK	LADY CONSTANCE, LADY MARGARET AND GIRLS
WOODEN TOYS, DOLLS, AND SMALL BOAT	CHILDREN
PITCHER	DENIS
BOW	ADAM
SMOCK, HOOD, LEG WRAPPINGS, LEATHER THONGS	ROBIN
HOOD	BRO. LUKE
PIKE	WELSH SENTRY
FIREWOOD	JOHN-GO-IN-THE-WYND
SIMULATED FIRE IN FIREPLACE	OLD WOMAN
COOKING POT	OLD WOMAN
SKILLET, CUPS, BOWLS, SPOONS, ETC.	OLD WOMAN
SLEEPING PALLET	ROBIN
HARP, KNIFE	JOHN-GO-IN-THE-WYND
SWORD	SIR PETER
NECKLACE	KING FOR ROBIN
SMALL STOOL, HARP	BRO. LUKE TO ROBIN

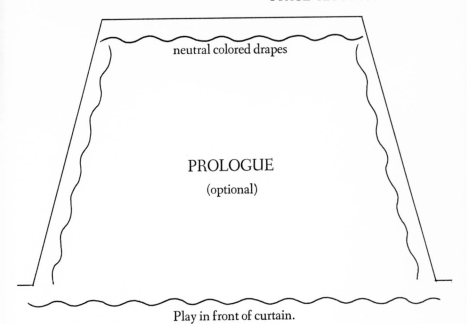

PROLOGUE

(optional)

Play in front of curtain.

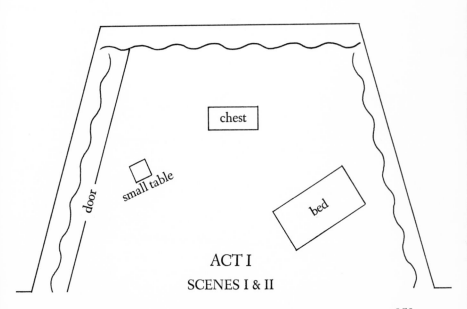

chest

small table

door

bed

ACT I

SCENES I & II

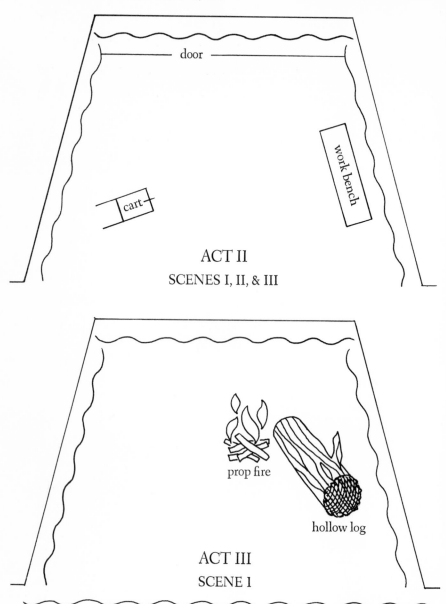

door

work bench

cart

ACT II

SCENES I, II, & III

prop fire

hollow log

ACT III

SCENE 1

First part played in front of curtain.
Blackout to denote passage of time.
Curtain is raised for balance of scene.

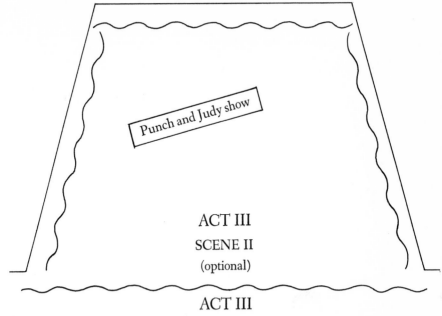

ACT III
SCENE II
(optional)

ACT III

SCENE III played in front of curtain.

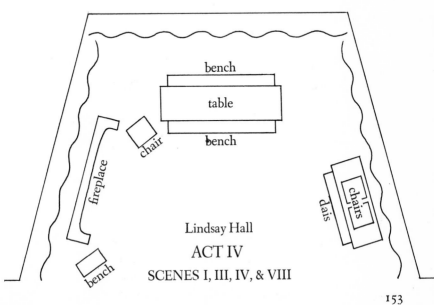

Lindsay Hall
ACT IV
SCENES I, III, IV, & VIII

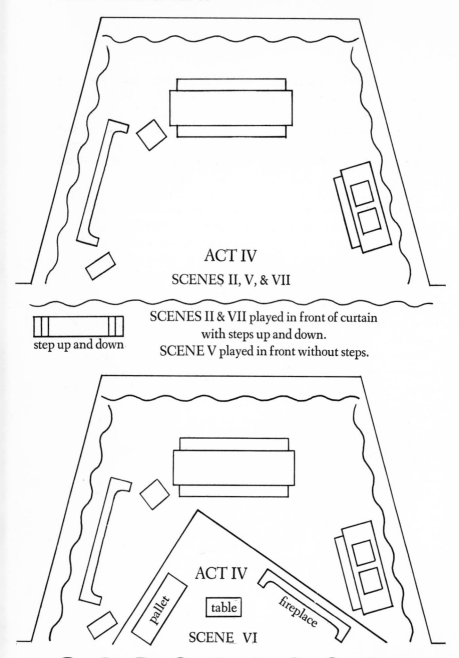

ACT IV

SCENES II, V, & VII

step up and down

SCENES II & VII played in front of curtain
with steps up and down.
SCENE V played in front without steps.

ACT IV

pallet

table

fireplace

SCENE VI

First part played in front of curtain.
Blackout. Curtain is raised for balance of scene.

ARTHUR CRAIG DE ANGELI was born in Philadelphia, Pennsylvania on North Fifty-fifth Street (which is the locale of Mrs. Marguerite de Angeli's *Turkey for Christmas*) on July 10th, 1912. He attended elementary school and high school in Collingswood, New Jersey, and later took extra courses in Jenkintown High School and attended Temple University. The most important specialized training he received was at the Rollins School of the Theatre in New York City.

Then followed approximately six years in the theater both as an actor and director, winding up this activity as a teacher, specializing in dramatics, of adult-education classes in and around Philadelphia.

While he continues to be active in non-professional theater, Mr. de Angeli is now professionally involved in the manufacture of plastic and metal items. He has formed a company with his two brothers, John and Harry, known as Helix, Inc. in Red Hill, Pennsylvania.

He is married to Nina Persichetti and they have a eighteen-year-old daughter, Kathryn Ann. The family lives on a small farm in the Upper Perkiomen Valley of Pennsylvania and raises thoroughbred horses.

Arthur de Angeli and daughter, Kate, are very active in the 4-H movement in Montgomery County, Pennsylvania, and both are enthusiastic fox hunters, belonging to two clubs in Chester County, Pennsylvania.

One of his hobbies is a continued interest in the theater as a director of amateur productions at the Dutch Country Playhouse near Green Lane, Pennsylvania.

Date Due
